Geography in Place 1

Michael Raw   **Sue Shaw**

Series Consultant: Nicholas Rowles

Collins Educational

An imprint of HarperCollins*Publishers*

Contents

Glossary words are highlighted in bold letters in the text the first time they appear.
* Indicates the more difficult exercises

1 Tectonic activity

EXERCISES

1 Study Figures 1.1 –1.3, 1.5. Make a list of the positive and negative effects of earthquakes and volcanoes for people.

1.1 Introduction

Earthquakes and volcanic eruptions are forces which shape the Earth's surface. They have awesome power (Fig.1.1). They not only shape the planet's surface but also affect the lives of millions of people. In this chapter we look at the causes of earthquakes and volcanoes, and their impact on the physical and human environment.

Fig. 1.1 Flyover destroyed by an earthquake in Japan.

Fig. 1.2 Cultivating rice on rich volcanic soil, Java.

Fig. 1.3 Geothermal power, Iceland.

Fig. 1.4 The structure of the earth.

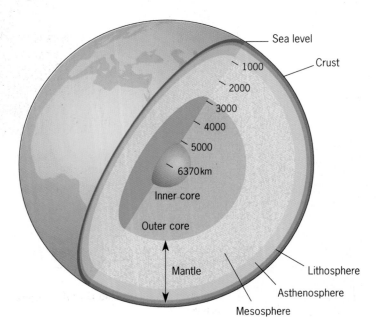

1.2 The interior of the Earth

We know very little about the Earth's interior. The world's deepest hole (in the Kola peninsula in Russia) only reaches 12 km below the surface. Most of what we know about the interior comes from studying earthquake waves. They show that the Earth is rather like an onion, made up of several concentric layers (Fig.1.4). At the surface there is a thin rocky layer or **crust** which forms the continents and ocean basins (Fig.1.6). Below the crust and attached to it is the **Lithosphere**. Deeper still is the **mantle** which occupies over 80 per cent of the Earth's volume. Finally, near the centre of the Earth there is the **core**. Each of these layers is different, due to its density, rock type and temperature (Table 1.1).

Table 1.1 Composition of the Earth

Layer		Depth of layer (km)	Average density (g/cm³)	Rock type	Temperature (°C)
					10
Crust	Continental	0–70	2.7	Granite	
	Oceanic	0–5	3.0	Basalt	
					375
Mantle		2900	5.5	Peridotite	
Core	Outer	2000	10.0	Iron/nickel (liquid)	
	Inner	1450	13.3	Iron/nickel (solid)	
					3000

1.3 Plate tectonics – the global conveyor

The earth's crust and lithosphere do not make a solid shell. In the mid-1960s American geologists discovered that the crust was broken into a number of large pieces or plates. They found seven major plates and dozens of smaller ones (Fig.1.7). This discovery led to an important new theory called **plate tectonics**, which helps to explain earthquakes, volcanoes, fold mountains, ocean trenches and many other landforms.

The central idea of plate tectonics is that the plates are moving all the time. However, this movement is only important along the plate edges, where two plates come together.

Plate tectonics recognises three types of plate margin. There are **constructive margins**, **destructive margins**, and **conservative margins**. At constructive margins new oceanic crust is formed. At destructive margins old oceanic crust is destroyed. But at conservative margins the crust is neither formed nor destroyed.

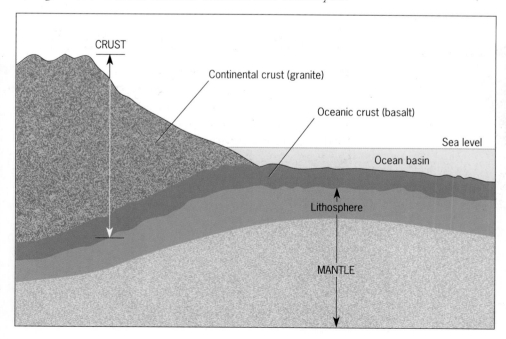

Fig. 1.5 The Strokkur geyser in south-west Iceland: a tourist attraction.

Fig. 1.6 The continental and oceanic crust.

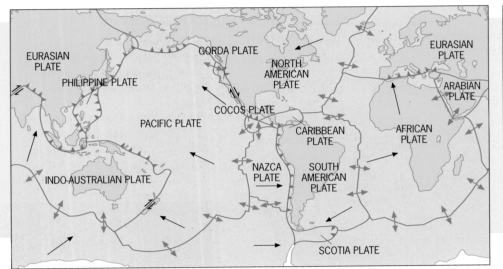

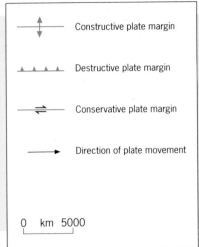

Constructive plate margin

▲▲▲▲ Destructive plate margin

⇄ Conservative plate margin

⟶ Direction of plate movement

0   km 5000

Fig. 1.7 The major lithospheric plates.

EXERCISES

3 Study Figure 1.7 and name the plates which contain the following geographical areas: British Isles; Scandinavia; Australia; South Asia; South-East Asia; Greenland; Madagascar.

Fig. 1.8 (left) Constructive plate margin (mid-ocean ridge).

Fig. 1.9 (right) Constructive plate margin in Iceland. The American plate is on the left and the Eurasian plate on the right.

Constructive plate margins

New crust forms in undersea valleys in mid-ocean. These valleys lie bounded by steep undersea mountain ranges called mid-ocean ridges (Fig.1.8). Here molten rock continually wells up from the mantle on to the ocean floor to create new crust. The new crust gradually pushes the older crust sideways, and away from the ridge. This sideways movement or sea-floor spreading is like a slow conveyor belt. It is as slow as the rate at which your finger nails grow! None the less, this movement adds up to a large distance over long periods of time. Thus in a million years new crust moves about 10 kilometres, and in 100 million years roughly 1000 kilometres.

Early in the 20th century many scientists suspected that the continents had not always been in their present position. However, they could not explain how areas as huge as continents could move across the globe. This was the puzzle of **continental drift**. Sea-floor spreading finally provided them with the answer. Because the continents are lighter than the oceanic crust, they ride on the conveyor of sea-floor spreading.

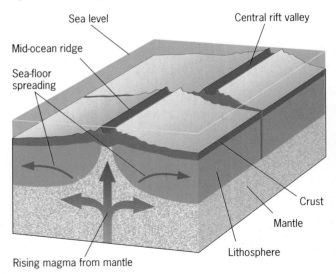

Destructive plate margins

We live on a planet whose size remains roughly the same, and yet sea-floor spreading tells us that new crust is constantly forming at the mid-ocean ridges. How is this possible? There is one simple answer: old crust must be destroyed at the same rate as new crust forms. To find out where this is happening, we once again have to look to the plate margins. Old crust is consumed at the destructive plate margins (Fig.1.7).

Sea-floor spreading gradually shifts oceanic crust away from the mid-ocean ridges until it reaches a **subduction zone** (Fig.1.11), this process typically takes around 200 million years. The subduction zone is where the crust (and lithosphere) plunge into the mantle. The zone is usually marked by a deep ocean trench. Subduction is accompanied by violent earthquakes and volcanic activity.

Conservative plate margins

At conservative boundaries no crust is added or destroyed. Instead the two plates which are in contact slide past each other with a shearing motion. This movement is not always smooth and easy. When there are sudden movements of the plates earthquakes occur. These earthquakes are just as severe as those at destructive plate boundaries.

Fig. 1.10 The Atlantic Ocean.

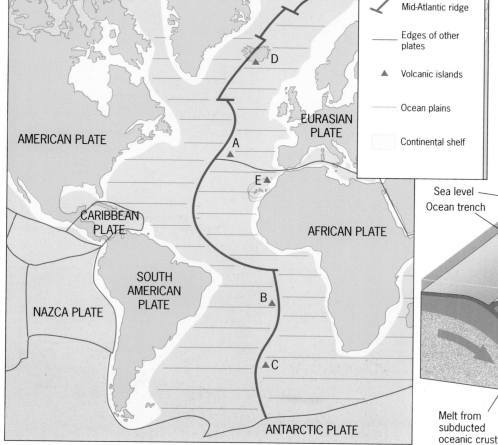

EXERCISES

3a Using an atlas, identify the islands A, B, C, D and E on Figure 1.10.
b How do you think these islands were formed?
c* Explain how Figure 1.10 might provide evidence of sea-floor spreading.
4a* Measure the width of the Atlantic Ocean at several points from the mid-ocean ridge to the coast of Europe and North America (Fig.1.10).
b* Calculate the average width in kilometres.
c* Assuming that sea-floor spreading averages 2.5 cm a year, approximately how old is the Atlantic Ocean?

EXERCISES

5* The most ancient rocks on the continents are around 3500 million years old. Read through the next section and suggest why the continental crust is so much older than the oceanic crust. (Clue: look at the density of the continents and ocean crust.)

Fig. 1.11 Destructive plate margin (subduction zone).

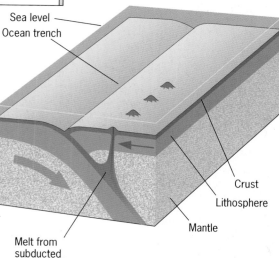

Darkness at dawn in India

Fear turns to reality as the Big One hits California

Inside the ruin that was once a city

Thousands flee ruins of Japanese quake city

City consumed by flames

1.4 Earthquakes – living on the edge

'The rising sun created darkness for us this morning, swallowed up our villages, and made our houses into tombs.'
Survivor from the earthquake in central India in 1993.

To geologists earthquakes are simply a natural event. However, for people like the Indian earthquake survivor, they are a human tragedy. They bring destruction, suffering and death, often without warning (Fig.1.12).

How earthquakes happen

An earthquake is the result of a sudden release of energy within the Earth which causes shocks or seismic waves. These seismic waves spread out from the origin or focus of the quake. The epicentre is the point of the Earth's surface immediately above the focus, and it is here that the destructive effects of the quake are greatest (Fig.1.13).

Fig. 1.12 Some newspaper headlines.

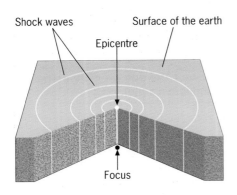

Seismic waves spread out from the focus of the earthquake and are recorded on seismometers which produce a trace. The peaks in the graph show the time when the earthquake shocks were recorded.

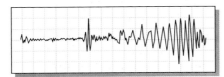

Fig. 1.13 Earthquake epicentre, focus and seismic trace.

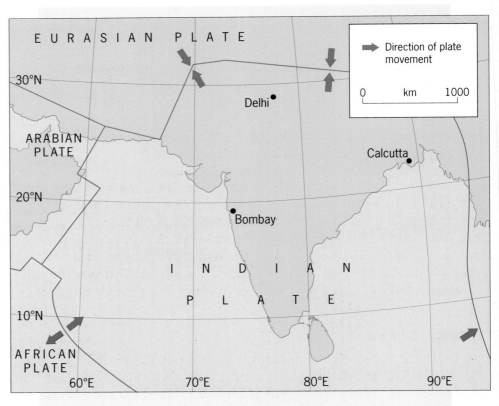

Fig. 1.14 Plate boundaries in South Asia.

Fig. 1.15 The San Andreas fault, California: a conservative plate margin.

Table 1.2 Indian earthquake, 30 September 1993

	Time of first shock waves	Time difference from epicentre	Distance from epicentre (t/60 x 1000)
Epicentre	03.56.00	0	0
Bombay	03.56.30	30 s	500 km
Delhi	03.57.15		
Calcutta	03.57.20		

Earthquakes occur when rocks, which have been compressed or stretched, snap along a fault in the crust. The best way to understand the origin of earthquakes is to plot quake epicentres on a world map showing the major plate boundaries (Fig.1.16). The epicentres lie mostly on the plate boundaries, which tells us that plate movements along plate margins are the key to earthquakes.

Mid-ocean ridges record many earthquakes, most of them near the surface. But the most destructive earthquakes are associated with subduction zones. Here where plates converge, one plate is forced downwards into the mantle. If this were a smooth process there would be no problem. However, the plate often becomes stuck on the surrounding mantle, causing enormous strain. Eventually the sudden release of the pressure creates powerful, deep-seated shock waves. This was the cause of several recent earthquakes such as those in Armenia (1988), India (1993) and Japan (1995).

Major earthquake zones

Probably the most celebrated earthquake zone in the world is in California. This region lies along a major fault line (San Andreas) which marks the edge of the North American and Pacific plates. Although California is on a conservative plate margin, it is a very active earthquake zone (Fig.1.15). There were large earthquakes in 1989 and 1993, and in 1906 the most severe earthquake of the twentieth century struck San Francisco, killing over 700 people.

EXERCISES

6 A severe earthquake struck India on 30 September 1993. In the area around the epicentre 10 000 people died. Study Figure 1.14 and suggest the possible cause of the Indian earthquake.

7 Find the epicentre of the Indian earthquake and give its approximate latitude and longitude. To determine the epicentre you need the following information:

• earthquake waves travel at a speed of 1000 km per minute.
• the time when the earthquake was recorded at its epicentre.
• the time when the shock waves were recorded at three other places (Table 1.2).

a Complete the calculations in Table 1.2.
b Make a copy of Figure 1.14 and draw three circles centred on Bombay, Delhi and Calcutta with radii proportional to their distance from the epicentre. The intersection of the circles gives the approximate epicentre.

1 Tectonic activity

EXERCISES

8 Name the two plates that meet along the San Andreas fault (Fig.1.7).

9 With the help of an atlas, find the location of the earthquakes in Table 1.3 (Fig.1.7). How many of these earthquakes are close to (a) destructive (b) constructive (c) conservative plate boundaries? Try to explain the distribution.

10 Using the information on deaths in Table 1.3, describe and explain the different effect that earthquakes have on rich countries (i.e. Japan, USA and Italy) and poor countries.

11* Plot a scattergraph of the death toll for each earthquake (*y* axis) in Table 1.3 against its magnitude (*x* axis). Describe the the relationship. Would you say that it was strong, moderate, weak or non-existent?

Fig. 1.16 The distribution of earthquakes around the world.

Table 1.3 Major earthquakes 1972 – 95 (Source: *The Guardian* 24.1.95)

Date	Location	Richter scale magnitude	Deaths
17.01.95	Japan	7.2	5000
15.02.94	Indonesia	6.5	37
17.01.94	Los Angeles, US	6.6	57
30.09.93	India	6.4	22 000
12.07.93	Japan	7.8	26
12.12.92	Indonesia	6.8	1912
28.06.92	California, US	7.4	1
25.04.92	California, US	6.9	0
13.03.92	Turkey	6.8	1000
01.02.91	Afghanistan/Pakistan border	6.8	1200
16.07.90	Philippines	7.7	1621
21.06.90	Iran	7.3-7.7	50 000
07.12.88	Armenia	6.9	25 000
19.09.85	Mexico	8.1	9500
30.10.83	Turkey	7.1	1300
13.12.82	North Yemen	6.0	2000
23.11.80	Italy	7.2	4800
10.10.80	Algeria	7.3	4500
12.12.79	Colombia and Ecuador	7.9	800
16.09.78	Iran	7.7	25 000
04.03.77	Romania	7.5	1541
24.11.76	Turkey	7.9	4000
17.08.76	Philippines	7.8	8000
28.07.76	Tangshan, China	7.8-8.2	242 000*/800 000**
06.05.76	Italy	6.5	946
04.02.76	Guatemala	7.5	22 778
06.09.75	Turkey	6.8	2312
10.04.72	Iran	6.9	5057

* official estimate **unofficial estimate

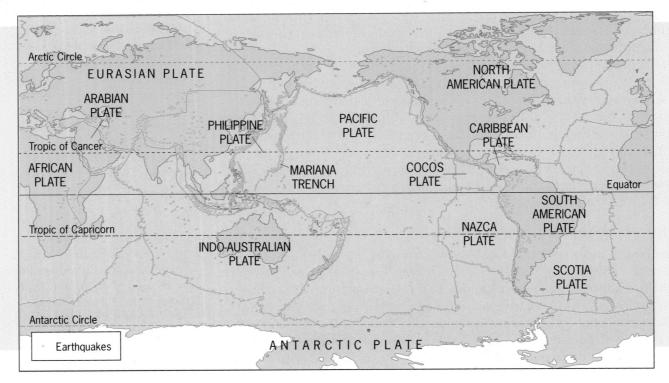

1.5 Kobe earthquake, Japan, 1995

By Japanese standards the earthquake which struck Kobe on 17 January 1995 was not unusually large; it measured 7.2 on the Richter scale (Table 1.5). And yet it devastated the city. It killed more than 5000 people, injured 25 000 and severely damaged 56 000 buildings. The city was not prepared because people thought that the area around Kobe was not as vulnerable to earthquakes as the Tokyo region.

Two factors help to explain the devastation the quake caused. First, the quake was shallow, with its focus near the surface. Second, its epicentre was close to Kobe (Fig.1.18). It was caused by movement along the subduction zone off the south coast of Japan where the Philippines plate underthrusts the Eurasian plate (Fig.1.17).

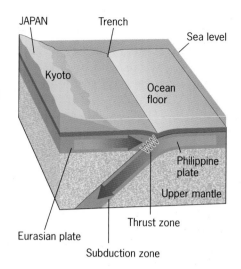

Fig. 1.17 Geology of the Kobe earthquake.

Fig. 1.18 The Kobe earthquake.

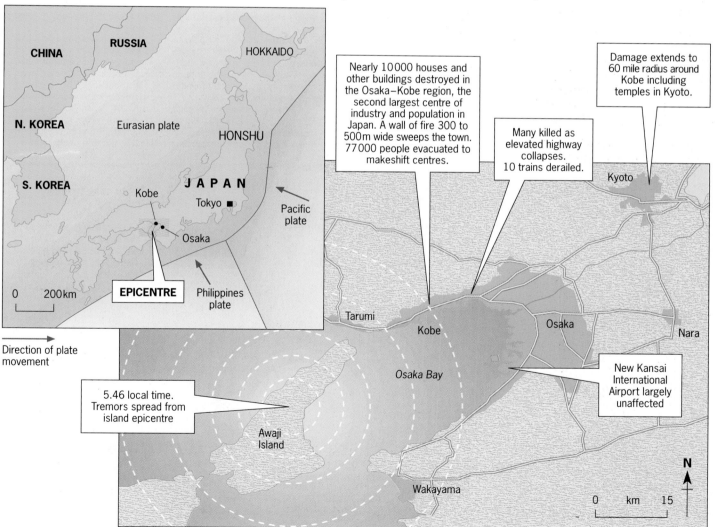

Nearly 10 000 houses and other buildings destroyed in the Osaka–Kobe region, the second largest centre of industry and population in Japan. A wall of fire 300 to 500 m wide sweeps the town. 77 000 people evacuated to makeshift centres.

Many killed as elevated highway collapses. 10 trains derailed.

Damage extends to 60 mile radius around Kobe including temples in Kyoto.

New Kansai International Airport largely unaffected

5.46 local time. Tremors spread from island epicentre

Direction of plate movement

Most older buildings in Kobe either collapsed or were badly damaged by the quake. Newer buildings, constructed to withstand earthquakes (Fig.1.20), remained standing, otherwise the loss of life would have been even greater. However, most deaths were caused by fires started by broken gas mains. In the days immediately after the quake there were shortages of water and food. Tens of thousands of people were left homeless in the Japanese winter. Disposal of dead bodies was delayed and, with no sewerage system, there was risk of disease. The disaster showed that earthquakes can devastate even the richest countries. Meanwhile, the long-term economic effects on Japan could be considerable: the damage and lost industrial output were estimated at US$90 billion.

Fig. 1.19 Report by Mark Dowdney, *Scottish Daily Record*, 18.1.95. (right)

Fig. 1.20 How to design buildings to resist earthquakes.

No escape in nightmare

A HUGE firestorm was last night threatening to turn quake-ravaged Kobe to ashes.

By MARK DOWDNEY

Hundreds of blazes swept through the Japanese city of 1.5 million people, after the tremor flattened 10,000 buildings in seconds.

More than 1700 people were confirmed dead. And with at least 1000 feared trapped in rubble, the toll was set to keep rising.

By last night, the growing inferno was threatening to rival the quake itself in savagery. Troops were called in to try to stem the destruction.

Survivors told how a 500 metre wide wall of flame swept through one area, fanned by strong winds.

Swathes of wooden houses were razed to the ground as gas mains ruptured and exploded.

With roads blocked by rubble, fire engines couldn't get to where they were most needed.

Crews who managed to reach fires quickly ran out of water, because the quake had destroyed main pipes. Many dazed and terrified residents had tried to save their homes with buckets of water, as aftershocks from the quake went on.

As night fell in Kobe, 12 hours had passed since the quake. More than 134 fires were still burning.

Crumbled

From the air, the busy port looked like it had been hit by a massive bombing raid. A deathly pall of smoke covered huge areas.

Kobe's hell began at dawn, when it was hit by Japan's worst earthquake in nearly 50 years.

The tremor, measured at 7.2 on the Richter scale, went on for 60 seconds of pure carnage.

A huge section of elevated motorway collapsed like a house of cards, hurling buses and cars to the ground. At least 14 people died.

Twenty trains were derailed. Bridges collapsed, and millions of people were left without water, gas, electricity or phone services.

Wharves at the harbour crumbled into the sea. A coach could be seen underwater.

One survivor, whose house collapsed around him, said: 'It felt like the end of the world.'

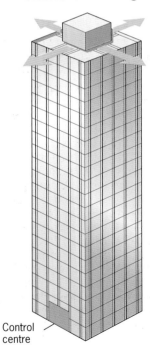

Concrete counter-weight

Control centre

A large concrete weight on top of the building controlled by computer moves in the opposite direction to the force of the earthquake.

A building that rocks back and forth

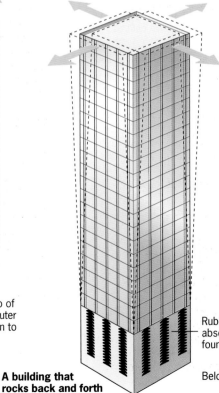

Large rubber shock absorbers in the foundations allow the building to rock back and forth and up and down without too much damage.

Rubber 'shock' absorbers in foundations

Below ground

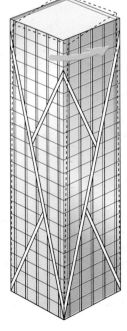

A twisting tower

Cross-bracings are added to the building which allow it to be more flexible and respond to the pressures caused by earthquakes.

In the 20th century about 1.4 million people have been killed in earthquakes. Most of these deaths were due to buildings collapsing. But today engineers are able to design buildings which can resist earthquakes.

EXERCISES

12 Estimate the magnitude of the Kobe earthquake on the Mercalli scale (Table 1.4).

13 Read Figure 1.19.
a Describe the impact of the Kobe quake on the city's infrastructure (roads electricity system etc.).
b What problems did earthquake damage pose for Kobe's emergency services?
c The earthquake struck at 05.46. How might this timing have helped to reduce the number of deaths and injuries?

14 Study Figure 1.20 and explain how modern buildings can be constructed to be earthquake-proof.

Fig. 1.21 A collapsed flyover in Kobe.

Table 1.4 Mercalli scale of earthquake intensity

Seismologists use the Mercalli scale to measure the physical effects of earthquakes. The scale goes from 1 (least effect) to 12 (greatest effect).

1 Rarely felt.
2 Felt by people who are not moving, especially on the upper floors of buildings. Hanging objects may swing.
3 The effects are noticeable indoors. The vibration is like that experienced when a truck passes.
4 Many people feel it indoors, a few outside. Some are awakened at night. Crockery and doors are disturbed, and standing cars rock.
5 Felt by nearly everyone. Most people are awakened. Some windows are broken, plaster becomes cracked and unstable objects topple. Trees may sway and pendulum clocks stop.
6 Felt by everyone. Many are frightened. Some heavy furniture moves, plaster falls. Structural damage is usually quite slight.
7 Everyone runs outdoors. Noticed by people driving cars. Poorly designed buildings are appreciably damaged.
8 Considerable amount of damage to ordinary buildings. Many buildings collapse; well designed ones survive with slight damage. Heavy furniture is overturned and chimneys fall. Some sand is fluidised.
9 Considerable damage occurs, even to buildings that have been well designed. Many buildings are moved from their foundations. Ground cracks and pipes break.
10 Most masonry structures are destroyed, some wooden ones survive. Railway tracks bend and water slops over banks. Landslides and sand movements occur.
11 No masonry structure remains standing. Bridges are destroyed. Broad fissures occur in the ground.
12 Total damage. Waves are seen on the surface of the ground. Objects are thrown into the air.

Table 1.5 Richter scale

The Richter scale is a precise measure of earthquake magnitude. However, unlike the Mercalli scale, it tells us nothing about an earthquake's destructive effects. Instruments called seismometers record earthquakes (a sensitive arm records the vibrations on a moving graph – see Fig.1.13) and these are scaled logarithmically. This means that an earthquake of magnitude 7 on the Richter scale is ten times more powerful than a magnitude 6 event, and 100 times more powerful than one of magnitude 5. The most powerful earthquake of the 20th century – the San Francisco quake in 1906 – measured 8.6 on the Richter scale.

Fig. 1.22 Pompeii in the shadow of Mount Vesuvius, a composite cone volcano.

Table 1.6 Catastrophic volcanic eruptions in the past

Year	Location	Effect
1500BC	Santorini, Greece	Island destroyed
AD 79	Vesuvius, Italy	Pompeii destroyed
1586	Kelud, Indonesia	10 000 dead
1669	Etna, Italy	20 000 dead
1815	Tambora, Indonesia	90 000 dead
1883	Krakatoa, Indonesia	36 000 dead
1902	Mont Pelee, Martinique	30 000 dead
1985	Nevado del Ruiz	25 000 dead

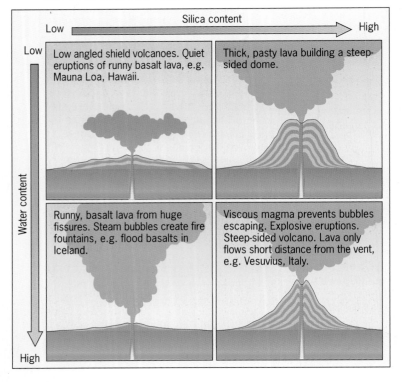

1.6 Volcanoes and volcanic eruptions

Volcanic eruptions are among the most spectacular and destructive events in nature. They change landscapes, the global weather and climate and, like earthquakes, they affect the lives of millions of people (Table 1.6).

Mount Vesuvius in southern Italy (Fig.1.22) is an active volcano which has erupted more than fifty times in the last 2000 years. Active volcanoes erupt molten rock or lava, ash, steam and hot gases. Layers of ash and lava from old eruptions eventually build up to form the classic cone-shaped volcano (Fig.1.22). However, not all volcanoes are cone-shaped. They come in a variety of shapes (Fig.1.23) which depend on the thickness (viscosity) of the lava. Thick, pasty lava, which doesn't flow very far, produces steep-sided volcanic domes. In contrast, thin runny lava may flow for many kilometres, building a low-angled shield volcano.

During eruptions, ash is pumped high into the atmosphere. The finest particles may remain suspended there for a year or more, blocking the sun's rays and disrupting the world's weather and climate. In 1815, Mount Tambora in Indonesia erupted, hurling several cubic kilometres of rock into the atmosphere. There was so much dust that it scattered and blocked the sunlight. In Europe in 1815, the harvests failed, there were frosts in June and July, and famine was widespread.

Sometimes volcanoes which have been inactive or dormant for hundreds of years suddenly burst into life. Mount Pinatubo in the Philippines erupted violently in 1991 having been dormant for 600 years. Indeed, some of the worst disasters have come from volcanoes that people thought were extinct, such as Vesuvius in AD 79, which devastated Pompeii.

However, not all eruptions come from volcanoes. In Iceland for example, fissure eruptions are common. Here molten rock quietly reaches the surface through great cracks in the Earth's crust. This type of eruption can form huge lava plateaus a kilometre or more in thickness. In the UK the best example is the Antrim plateau in Northern Ireland (Fig.1.24).

Fig. 1.23 Different types of volcanoes and eruptions.

Distribution of volcanoes

There are more than 600 active volcanoes in the world (Fig.1.25). Indonesia alone has more than one hundred. The greatest concentration of volcanic activity is around the Pacific Ocean. In the western Pacific the so-called 'ring of fire' extends from Kamchatka in Russia, through Japan, the Philippines and Indonesia. In the eastern Pacific it follows the Andean and Rocky mountain ranges. Finally, in the north, the chain of volcanic islands known as the Aleutians completes the ring, by linking North America and Eurasia (Fig.1.26).

Fig. 1.24 Columnar basalt: the Giant's Causeway in Antrim, Northern Ireland.

Fig. 1.25 The world distribution of active volcanoes.

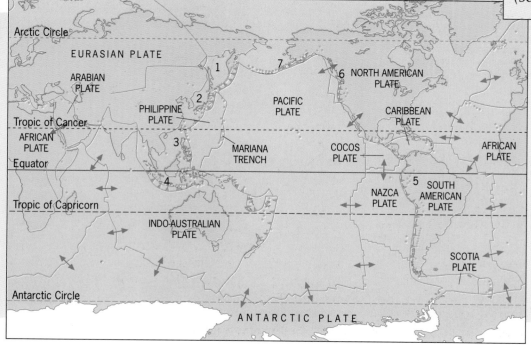

Table 1.7 Volcanoes and plate margins

Volcano	Type of plate margin
Fuji	
St Helens	
Cotopaxi	
Etna	
Pinatubo	
Mauna Loa	
Hood	
Hekla	
Aconcagua	
Krakatoa	
Surtsey	
Tristan da Cunha	

EXERCISES

15 a Use an atlas to find the location of the volcanoes listed in Table 1.7.
b Refer to Figure 1.25 and decide which volcanoes are located at conservative and which at destructive plate margins. Make a copy of Table 1.7 and insert the type of plate margin beside each volcano.
c* How is the location of Mauna Loa different from the other volcanoes in Table 1.7? Can you explain its location? (See Figure 1.30.)

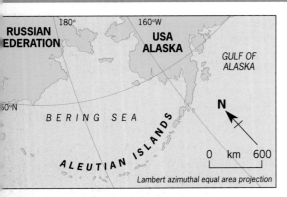

1.7 Causes of volcanic eruptions

Volcanic eruptions occur where molten rock from the mantle reaches the surface. Most eruptions take place on or close to plate boundaries. What is happening in these areas to cause eruptions?

First remember that, geologically, plate margins are very active places. Here new crust forms, and old crust is destroyed. Along the mid-ocean ridges where the crust is being stretched and the plates are pulled apart, molten rock welling up from the mantle, spills on to the ocean floor. In Iceland we can actually see this happening on the land

Fig. 1.26 A volcanic island arc.

Fig. 1.27 A basalt lava flow from Kilauea volcano, Hawaii.

Fig. 1.28 Parinacota and Pomerape volcanoes in the Andes.

Fig. 1.29 Flood basalts in Oregon, USA.

Island arcs
Where two oceanic plates converge (e.g. western Pacific). One plate is pushed downwards (subducted) into the mantle. As the subducted plate melts, magma rises to the surface forming numerous volcanoes or island arcs, e.g. the Aleutian Islands.

Mid-oceanic ridges
Tension in the crust leads to deep rifts. Magma rises up to the ocean floor along these rifts, forming new crust. The ridges form a continuous line of submarine volcanoes. In places the volcanoes rise above sea level, e.g. Iceland.

Hot spot volcanoes
Rising plumes of magma reach the surface in the centres of plates, e.g. Hawaii.

Continental-ocean plate margins.
Here the oceanic plate is subducted beneath the thicker continental plate. As it melts some of the lighter oceanic plate magma forces its way to the surface, forming volcanoes, e.g. Andean volcanoes.

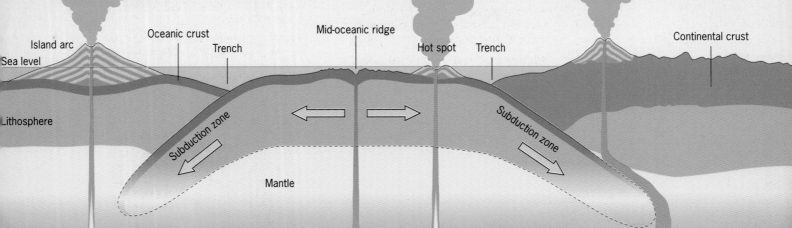

Fig. 1.30 Causes of volcanic eruptions.

2 Rocks and landscapes

2.1 Introduction

Rocks form the 'bones' of the landscape. In the uplands this is obvious: here rocks are often exposed at the surface and are plain to see (Fig. 2.1). But in the lowlands and in large cities you cannot normally see rocks. They are usually hidden beneath roads and buildings and thick layers of soil. In this chapter we shall try to answer some very basic questions concerning rocks. For instance: What are rocks? How are they formed? What effect do they have on **relief** and the landscape? How are they altered by **weathering** and **erosion**, and the tectonic forces which we studied in Chapter 1?

2.2 Types of rock

We can think of rocks as being like a fruit cake. A fruit cake has ingredients such as sugar, sultanas, nuts and so on, and in the same way rocks are a mixture of minerals such as quartz, calcite and feldspar.

Many rocks have mineral mixtures that are similar. This enables us to recognise different kinds of rock. Granite, for example, consists of just three minerals: quartz, feldspar and mica. Limestone is even simpler: often it contains just one mineral - calcium carbonate.

Although there are hundreds of different kinds of rock, we can group them all into three main types: **igneous**, **sedimentary** and **metamorphic.** We base this simple classification on how the rocks have been formed (Fig. 2.2).

Fig. 2.1 Rock type can affect the relief of an area – old hard rocks at Glenfinnan, north-west Scotland.

EXERCISES

1 Find out:
a The nearest place where you can see bare rock at the surface.
b What type of rock is it?
c Why does it appear in that place?
d Does the rock outcrop have any effect on the relief?

2 The landscape in Figure 2.1 is made of igneous rock. Using the evidence of the photograph suggest two reasons why this rock is resistant to weathering and erosion.

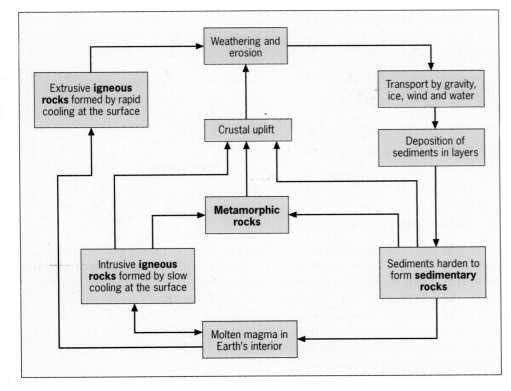

Fig. 2.2 How rocks are formed.

Fig. 2.3 The mineral structure of granite.

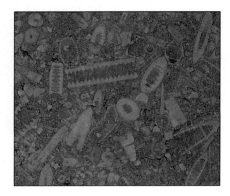

Fig. 2.4 Fossilised remains in limestone.

Fig. 2.5 Joints and bedding planes in sedimentary rocks.

Fig. 2.6 Marble, which is metamorphosed limestone.

Igneous rocks

Some igneous rocks result from volcanic activity. All start out as magma, before they cool and solidify. Cooling occurs either at the Earth's surface or within the **crust**. Where magma reaches the surface, it forms lava, which cools rapidly. As a result lavas such as basalt consist of tiny mineral crystals, which you cannot see with the naked eye.

Granite is a common igneous rock and forms most of the continental crust. Unlike basalt, granite cooled slowly deep inside the earth's crust. This meant that large mineral crystals had time to develop, making the rock extremely coarse-grained (Fig.2.3) and resistant to erosion.

Sedimentary rocks

Most sedimentary rocks consist of tiny particles (mud, sand, clay). These were formed by the breakdown of rocks on the Earth's surface . The broken rock particles were then carried away by wind, rivers or ice and usually deposited on the sea floor. In general, sedimentary rocks are more easily eroded than igneous rocks. Some, like shale or mudstone, you can easily break by hand.

Limestone, chalk and coal differ from other sedimentary rocks because they are formed from the remains of plants and animals which lived millions of years ago. Limestone and chalk are made of the shells and skeletons of tiny sea creatures whose remains built up on the sea bed. Coal is the fossilised remains of ancient plants such as trees.

Unlike igneous and metamorphic rocks, sedimentary rocks were laid down in sheets or layers – known as **strata**. Each layer is separated from those above and below it by a **bedding plane** (Fig.2.5). When sedimentary rocks first formed, the bedding planes were usually horizontal. However, it is common to find sedimentary rocks with tilted bedding planes. This tells us that the rocks were disturbed by great earth movements after they were formed.

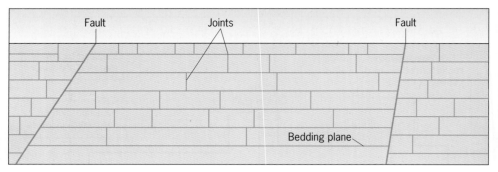

Metamorphic rocks

Metamorphic rocks have been changed either by great heat or great pressure. For instance, when a huge mass of molten granite is **intruded** into the crust, it alters the surrounding rocks. Thus, limestone in contact with the hot granite may be baked or metamorphosed into marble (Fig. 2.6). Pressure has a similar effect, but on a larger scale, changing rocks over a much wider area. For example, the slates of the Lake District and North Wales were once shales and mudstones which have been metamorphosed by pressure.

Table 2.1 Identifying types of rock

Rock	Formation	Rock type
Granite	Molten rock intruded into the crust and cooled slowly.	
Limestone	Remains of the shells and skeletons of small creatures deposited on the sea floor (Fig. 2.4).	
Coal	Fossilised remains of trees and other plants.	
Sandstone	Sand-sized particles compressed and cemented together.	
Basalt	Runny lava erupted from a volcano which is cooled quickly at the Earth's surface.	
Marble	Limestone changed by great heat and pressure (Fig. 2.6).	
Slate	Shales and clays changed by great pressure.	

Fig. 2.7 (below left) Distribution of rock types in the British Isles.

Fig. 2.8 (below right) The relief of the British Isles.

EXERCISES

2a Make a larger copy of Table 2.1. Complete the table by identifying each rock type as igneous, sedimentary or metamorphic.
b* Which type of rock – igneous or sedimentary – is most likely to be altered by metamorphism? Give reasons for your answer.

EXERCISES

3 Study Figures 2.7 and 2.8
a Describe the distribution of igneous and metamorphic rocks in Britain.
b Describe how the distribution of rock types in Britain is related to relief.
c Suggest an explanation for this relationship.

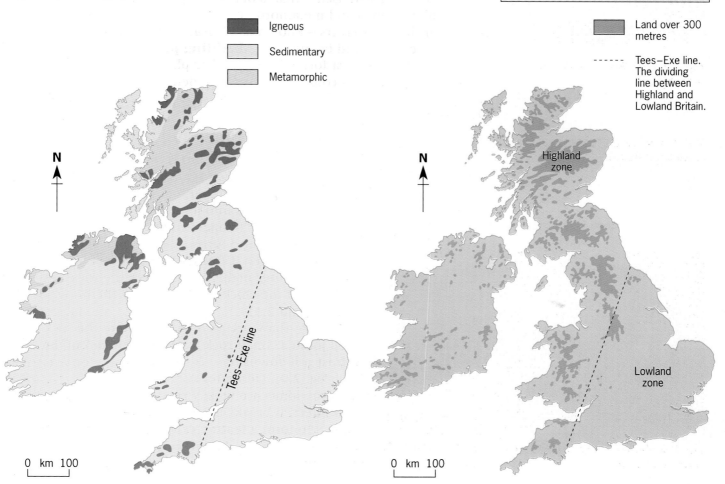

Igneous
Sedimentary
Metamorphic

Land over 300 metres

Tees–Exe line. The dividing line between Highland and Lowland Britain.

N

Tees–Exe line

0 km 100

N

Highland zone

Lowland zone

0 km 100

Fig.2.9 Screes and scars in Littondale, North Yorkshire.

Fig. 2.10 A gritstone block split by frost action, Norber, North Yorkshire.

2.11 A granite blockfield in the Cairngorm plateau.

2.3 Rock structure

We often use the term 'rock hard' for something that is very difficult to break. This description fits most rocks, especially igneous and metamorphic ones. And yet along the coast and in the uplands we often come across large areas of rock (Figs 2.9 and 2.11) which have been broken up by natural forces such as waves and frost.

This suggests that rocks are not always as tough as they seem. The reason is that rocks have cracks and lines of weakness called joints and bedding planes (Fig.2.5). We call this the rock's structure. It is here that the processes of weathering and erosion act most strongly. Given enough time, even the hardest rocks are eventually broken down.

2.4 Weathering

Rocks which are found at or near the surface experience changes in heat and moisture. Slowly these changes cause the rocks to break down by a process called weathering. Some types of weathering simply break up the rocks into smaller fragments. This is physical weathering. In contrast, chemical weathering causes breakdown by altering the minerals in rocks.

Rocks are also eroded by ice, wind, water and the action of animals and plants.

Physical weathering

In high latitudes, frost action is the most common type of physical weathering. Consider what happens to rainwater falling on to a rock surface in winter. First it seeps into joints and cracks in the rocks. Then, if the temperature drops below zero, the water freezes and turns to ice. Water expands by 9 per cent when it freezes (which in the uplands is on most winter nights). This forces the rocks on either side of the cracks apart, causing them to split (Figs.2.10 and 2.11).

If freeze-thaw occurs on a cliff where the rock is well jointed, small rock fragments broken off by the frost roll downslope. They build up to form scree (Fig. 2.9). On flatter surfaces, especially where the joints are widely spaced, frost has a different effect. It breaks up the rock into massive boulders to form a feature called a **blockfield** (Fig.2.11).

2 Rocks and landscapes

Tree roots also cause physical weathering. They penetrate and widen rock joints (Figs. 2.12 and 2.14). And, if a tree topples over in a gale, its roots may lift out great blocks of rock.

In hot deserts like the Sahara, where there is little plant cover, we find a different type of physical weathering. Insolation weathering occurs when rocks are exposed to the powerful rays of the sun in the day and to rapid cooling at night. The surface minerals of rocks heat up and expand at different rates. This sets up stresses, weakening the rock and causing the outer layers to peel away. The effect is much greater if the rock is occasionally wetted by rain, dew or mist. This process is known as **exfoliation** or 'onion peel' weathering and produces boulders and rock outcrops with unusual rounded shapes (Fig.2.13).

Fig. 2.12 Biological weathering by a tree's roots.

Fig. 2.13 Exfoliated granite rocks in California.

Fig. 2.14 Rocks shattered by the roots of a fallen tree.

Chemical weathering

Chemical weathering takes place both on the surface and below it, wherever moisture is present. It covers a wide range of complex chemical reactions which alter rock minerals and cause the rocks to disintegrate.

One of the most common forms of chemical weathering is solution. Some rock minerals, such as calcium carbonate, dissolve easily in water that contains carbon dioxide. Others react with oxygen (oxidation) or water, and are weakened and break down. Nearly all of these processes operate best at high temperatures. That is why chemical weathering is most common in warm climates, especially those around the Equator, which are both warm and wet.

EXERCISES

4 Draw a sketch of Figure 2.9 to explain how frost action on a cliff face causes weathering and the formation of scree.
5 List the different types of weathering taking place in each of the areas shown in Figures 2.10 – 2.14

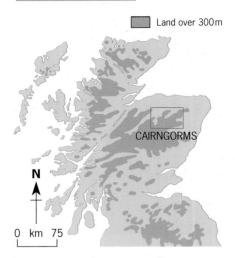

Land over 300m

Fig. 2.15 The location of the Cairngorms.

EXERCISES

6 Given the climate of the Cairngorms, what types of weathering would you expect to find there? Explain your answer.

Fig. 2.16 A granite tor in the Cairngorms.

2.5 Granite landscape: the Cairngorms

The Cairngorms in north-east Scotland form a plateau over 1200 metres high which contains four of the five highest mountains in the British Isles (Fig. 2.15). The plateau has a severe, almost arctic-like climate. Its average annual temperature is just below freezing, which allows patches of snow to survive throughout the summer. (If the world's climate were to cool by a degree or so, these snow patches would quickly become glaciers.)

The Cairngorms are made entirely from granite, one of the toughest of all rocks. The granite is part of a huge mass called a **batholith** which was originally intruded deep inside the crust. Slowly, over millions of years, the less resistant rocks above the granite have been stripped away. Now at the surface the granite can be eroded (Fig.2.17).

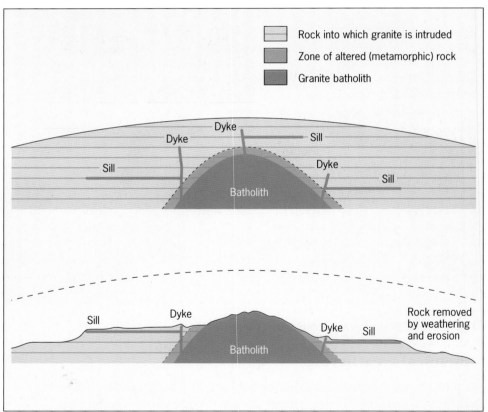

Rock into which granite is intruded

Zone of altered (metamorphic) rock

Granite batholith

Fig. 2.17 Formation of a batholith.

Because granite is so hard, it is eroded much more slowly than the surrounding less resistant rocks. As a result the Cairngorms form a plateau, which dominates the relief of that part of Scotland. Around the edges of the plateau glaciers have carved deep U-shaped valleys. Vertical cliffs on the valley sides have been weathered by frost action, leaving screes and boulder fields on the lower slopes. There are glacial deposits on the valley floor .

Meanwhile, on the plateau surface, frost has broken the granite into a chaotic boulder-strewn landscape forming blockfields (Fig.2.11). Also, on high ground, isolated outcrops of granite called tors rise above the plateau surface (Fig.2.16). Geologists think that these features were formed mainly by chemical weathering. This weathering was concentrated on where the vertical joints were close together (Fig.2.18). Later, erosion removed the weathered granite, and frost action dislodged large blocks of granite from the tors.

Fig. 2.18 (right) Formation of a granite tor.

Fig. 2.19 (below) 1:50 000 OS map extract of the Cairngorms.

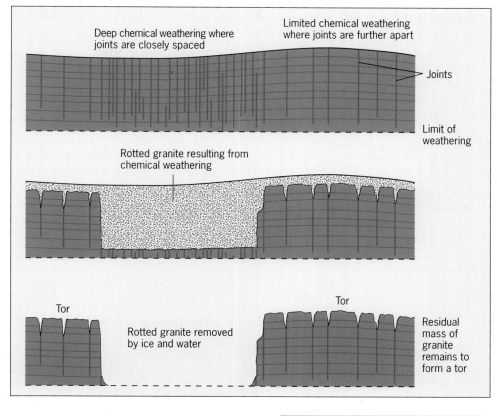

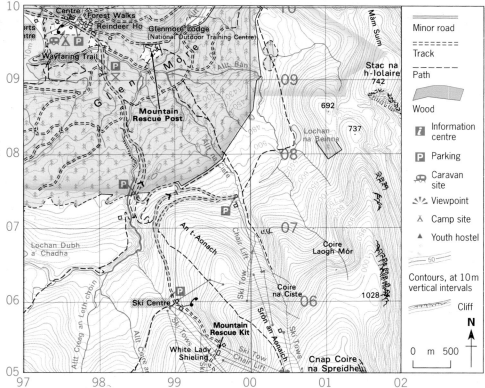

7 Study Figure 2.19.

a Give six-figure references and the height for three high points on the map.

b* What evidence suggests that the rock type in some areas might be granite?

c What evidence can you find for tourism in this area? Give examples and grid references.

d With reference to the map, name one recreational activity other than skiing.

e* Using Figure 2.19, explain how the physical geography of the Cairngorms influences recreation in the area.

f What types of work would be available to people who live in this area? Give examples from the map.

Minor igneous intrusions and the landscape

Areas of igneous rock which cooled slowly within the Earth's crust are known as intrusions. Some of these intrusions such as the granite batholiths of the Cairngorms and Dartmoor, are huge. Others are small. These minor intrusions are called **sills** and **dykes** (Fig.2.17).

Sills are sheets of igneous rock (especially dolerite) which have been forced between the bedding planes of older rocks. They often cover large areas. Because dolerite is usually harder than the surrounding rock, it often forms steep slopes. On valley sides a sill may crop out as a cliff. Where it crosses a river, it creates a band of resistant rock and forms a waterfall. One of the best-known sills in the British Isles is the Great Whin Sill of northern England. It has a strong influence on the landscape in this region. It forms the steep ridge along which part of Hadrian's Wall (built in Roman times) runs (Figs 2.20 and 2.21). It also forms the Farne islands and High Force, the highest waterfall in England.

Dykes are similar to sills, except that they cut across the bedding planes of older rocks. As a result they crop out vertically, in long narrow bands, which sometimes run for tens of kilometres across the landscape.

Fig. 2.20 (right) An aerial view of the Roman Wall at Housesteads.

Fig. 2.21 (below) A geological section through the Whin Sill at Housesteads.

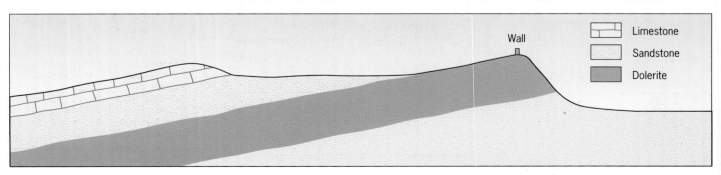

2.6 Limestone landscape: the Yorkshire Dales

In the Yorkshire Dales (Fig.2.27) a hard mountain limestone known as Carboniferous Limestone is found. This rock slowly dissolves in rainwater. How does this chemical weathering happen?

As rain falls from clouds and soaks into the soil, it absorbs carbon dioxide to become dilute carbonic acid. This acid then reacts with the main mineral in Carboniferous Limestone – calcium carbonate – to make calcium bicarbonate, which is carried off in solution. The rock is dissolved at a rate of about 4 cm every 1000 years. This acidic solution acts most strongly on the lines of weakness (i.e. joints).

Fig. 2.22 (above) A limestone pavement at Conistone in Upper Wharfedale, North Yorkshire.

Fig. 2.23 (below) The formation of karst scenery.

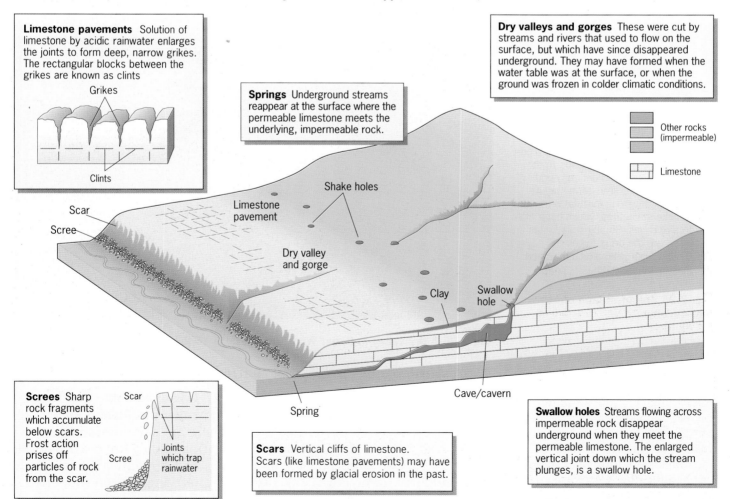

Limestone pavements Solution of limestone by acidic rainwater enlarges the joints to form deep, narrow grikes. The rectangular blocks between the grikes are known as clints

Grikes

Clints

Dry valleys and gorges These were cut by streams and rivers that used to flow on the surface, but which have since disappeared underground. They may have formed when the water table was at the surface, or when the ground was frozen in colder climatic conditions.

Springs Underground streams reappear at the surface where the permeable limestone meets the underlying, impermeable rock.

Other rocks (impermeable)

Limestone

Scar

Scree

Shake holes

Limestone pavement

Dry valley and gorge

Clay

Swallow hole

Spring

Cave/cavern

Screes Sharp rock fragments which accumulate below scars. Frost action prises off particles of rock from the scar.

Scar

Scree

Joints which trap rainwater

Scars Vertical cliffs of limestone. Scars (like limestone pavements) may have been formed by glacial erosion in the past.

Swallow holes Streams flowing across impermeable rock disappear underground when they meet the permeable limestone. The enlarged vertical joint down which the stream plunges, is a swallow hole.

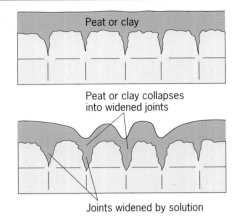

Peat or clay

Peat or clay collapses into widened joints

Joints widened by solution

Shake holes Funnel-shaped hollows found where the limestone has a cover of peat or boulder clay.

Fig. 2.24 How shake holes form.

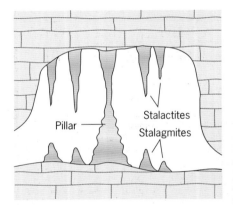

Pillar

Stalactites

Stalagmites

Caves and caverns The solution along joints and bedding planes leads to the formation of caves and underground features. Dissolved limestone may be deposited as dripstone (or tufa) in the form of finger-like stalactites, which hang from the roofs of caves. Stubby stalagmites are built up where the drips fall on the cave floor. Pillars form when stalactites and stalagmites join together.

Fig. 2.25 The formation of caves and caverns.

EXERCISES

9a Study Figure 2.26 and draw a sketch of the valley. Add the following labels: dry valley, scree, and cliff.
b* Include a few notes on your sketch explaining how these features were formed and possible difficulties for farming in this area.

The result of solution is a distinctive type of scenery known as **karst** (Fig.2.23). (It is named after a limestone area in Croatia.) On level surfaces, where the soil and rocks covering the limestone were scoured by ice sheets, there are limestone pavements (Fig.2.22). These pavements consist of bare rock, broken into rectangular blocks or clints. Between the clints are deep cracks known as grikes. The grikes are simply joints which have been widened by solution. The edge of the pavement is often marked by a small cliff or scar.

Limestone is a permeable rock. Rain water quickly seeps underground along its many vertical joints. As a result, limestone areas have very few surface streams. However, in the past when the climate was much colder, and the ground was permanently frozen, streams did flow on the surface. The evidence for this is the many dry valleys that we see in limestone areas (Fig.2.26). Today streams only flow in these valleys after periods of very heavy rain.

Hidden below the surface there is a complex drainage system of streams, caves and caverns. Streams flowing on to the limestone soon disappear underground down enlarged joints or swallow holes. Springs occur where underground streams re-emerge at the surface. Meanwhile those streams which do run on the surface often flow in gorges with almost vertical sides. It is likely that these gorges have developed because there is so little surface water on the limestone slopes to wear down the valley sides.

Fig 2.26 A dry valley in Upper Wharfedale, North Yorkshire.

Limestone quarrying: conservation or jobs?

Limestone is a valuable mineral (Table 2.2). It is so valuable that it is quarried in some of the most beautiful landscapes in England which are supposedly protected as National Parks. There are eight limestone quarries in the Yorkshire Dales National Park and they are controversial. They destroy the landscape, are an eyesore, and generate a lot of noise, dust and lorry traffic (Fig.2.28). However, quarrying is often supported by local people because it creates much-needed jobs.

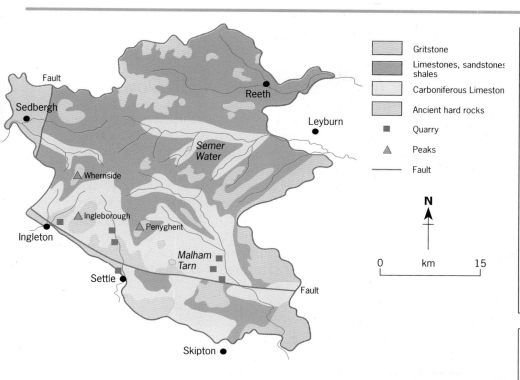

2.27 Yorkshire Dales National Park. (above)

Gritstone
Limestones, sandstones shales
Carboniferous Limeston
Ancient hard rocks
■ Quarry
▲ Peaks
— Fault

N

0   km   15

EXERCISES

10 Read Figures 2.28 and 2.29.
a What will the quarry owners do to reduce inconvenience to residents, and damage to the environment?
b In your own words summarise the views of those in favour, and those against the proposal.
c The issue of quarrying is about the conflict between jobs for local people and conservation. What is your view on this issue? Briefly state your opinion and then explain why you hold it.

'There is no doubt that the extent of present quarrying has scarred our landscape and pollution by dust and of water has been significant. But quarry companies today fully realise the need to be good neighbours and take all possible measures to minimise inconvenience.'

Local councillor

'If we allow this we will be continuing the misery for those people who live in the area and risking their water supply. There are only seven employees resident in the National Park on the company's payroll.'

Local resident

'We are trying to give local employment some protection. We are talking about wage earners, who aren't very highly paid, who support a family. These are hardworking Dales people.'

Local councillor

'My 11 hectares of land are likely to be flooded as there will be a 78 per cent increase in water going down the Beck. The Beck just won't be able to take it.'

Local farmer

The development is contrary to what should be the policy of the national parks, to look after our finest landscapes.

Secretary, Craven branch of the Council for the Protection of Rural England

'Much of the material extracted from the quarry will be used as aggregate to make more roads to further destroy the countryside. The great majority of people in Cracoe will be disappointed.'

Chairman of the parish council

'Local residents will benefit from the visual improvement and reduced hours of transport. There will be a cessation of almost all night-time lorries leaving the quarry'

Spokeswoman for quarry company

Quarry extension wins approval

Chairman uses casting vote to decide contentious plan

by Sue Marshall

Quarrying at Cracoe is set to continue to the year 2000 after the national park gave the go-ahead to Tilcon's controversial plans to push extraction 100 metres deeper into the bowels of Swinden Quarry.

Following a two hour debate on Tuesday the park's planning committee was evenly split with the balance tipped in Tilcon's favour by chairman Robert Heseltine's casting vote.

Initial extraction will be at the Threshfield end of the quarry and in five to six years time plant and machinery will be hidden from view. Landscaping will restore much of the hillside and Tilcon has set aside £500,000 to help turn the site into a nature reserve on completion of quarrying. Officers had recommended refusal of the scheme to extract a further 37 million tonnes of Dales limestone on the grounds that it contravened environmental and traffic policies.

They felt there were already adequate reserves of stone and the development could not be carried out without detriment to water supplies.

But Tilcon has pledged to sink new bore holes should the supply be affected and ward councillor Shelagh Marshall proposed the plan be approved.

Fig. 2.29 (above) Report by Sue Marshall in the Craven Herald and Pioneer, 17 March, 1995.

Fig. 2.28 (left) Reactions to Swinden Quarry.

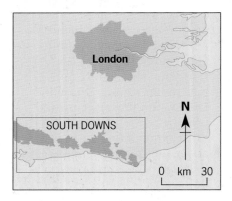

Fig. 2.30 The location of the South Downs.

2.7 Chalk landscape: the South Downs

Chalk is a soft type of limestone. It is also **porous** because it contains tiny air spaces or pores between its mineral particles which absorb water, rather like a sponge. As a result there are very few permanent streams and rivers in chalklands.

This lack of surface water has always been a problem for settlement in these areas (see Chapter 5). It has forced settlements to cluster around springs where there is a permanent water supply. There are two places where springs are often found in chalklands: at the foot of scarp slopes, where the chalk rests on an impermeable rock such as clay, and on dip slopes, where the zone of saturated rock (**water table**) reaches the surface (Fig.2.31).

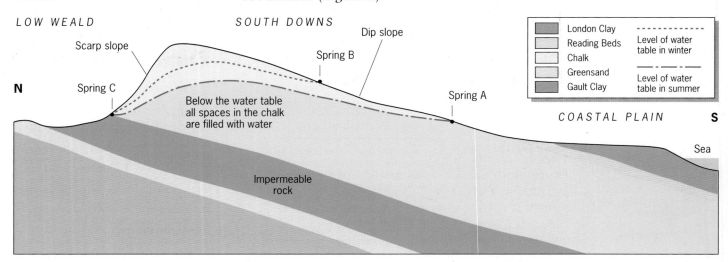

Fig. 2.31 The water table in the chalk escarpment.

The South Downs are a line of chalk hills or an **escarpment** stretching from Hampshire, to Beachy Head near Brighton (Figs.2.30 and 2.36). Although the Downs are on average only 200 metres high, they are an impressive feature. Most striking is the steep, north-facing scarp slope rising abruptly from the Low Weald (Fig.2.31). Beyond the scarp, a gentle dip slope runs down to the Channel coast. In several places the escarpment is cut by the valleys of southward-flowing rivers such as the Arun, Ouse and Cuckmere.

How can chalk, which is a less resistant rock, form such a prominent relief feature? There are two answers. Firstly, the surrounding rocks (Figs.2.31 and 2.36) are more easily eroded than chalk and are therefore worn down more quickly. Secondly, because streams and rivers are rare in chalklands today, the chalk is no longer being worn away by rivers. However, this was not always so. The dip slope of the South Downs is criss-crossed by a network of dry valleys. They formed during the ice age when the chalk was permanently frozen, which allowed rivers to flow on the surface during the brief arctic summers.

Fig. 2.32 An aerial view of the South Downs near Truleigh Hill, Sussex.

2.8 Clay landscapes

Clay is a less resistant material. Because it is so easily worn down by rivers and glaciers, it often forms lowlands with gentle slopes. In northern Britain and East Anglia many lowlands are covered with a thick layer of till or boulder clay. This sticky, easily moulded material was left behind over 13 000 years ago by great ice sheets and glaciers. In southern Britain, the clay is much older. It is sandwiched between more resistant rocks like chalk and limestone. This clay often forms broad vales such as the Vale of Oxford and the Vale of the White Horse in Wiltshire.

Table 2.2 The economic value of rocks

Rock type	Economic value and use
Granite	Upland areas with steep slopes and poor soils. Rough grazing for sheep. Water catchment. Recreation (hill walking, climbing). Quarrying for roadstone, ornamental stone and china clay.
Limestone	Quarrying for roadstone, lime for cement, steelmaking etc. Thin soils and lack of surface water support only rough grazing and pasture land for sheep and cattle. Many limestone areas (Yorkshire Dales, Peak District, Mendips) are very scenic and are important for recreation.
Chalk	Lack of water and thin soils. Not much settlement. Mainly rough grazing and permanent pasture, though better soils may be cultivated. Chalk is quarried for lime and cement.
Dolerite	Mainly quarried for roadstone. Outcrops of dolerite cover only small areas and therefore have little effect on land use.
Clay	Produces heavy soils suitable for livestock farming, especially dairying and beef. Clay (e.g. Gault Clay and Wealden Clay, Fig. 2.36) is quarried to make bricks in many parts of the UK.

Fig. 2.33 Folded limestone rocks, Dorset.

2.9 Folding and faulting

Folding

At first, most sedimentary rocks form in horizontal layers. Sometimes these rocks lay undisturbed for millions of years. We know this because today many layers are still in their original horizontal position. Often, however, tectonic forces within the crust (see Chapter 1) compress the rocks and fold them into new shapes. These forces have **folded** sedimentary rocks into some of the highest mountains ranges in the world (Fig.2.38).

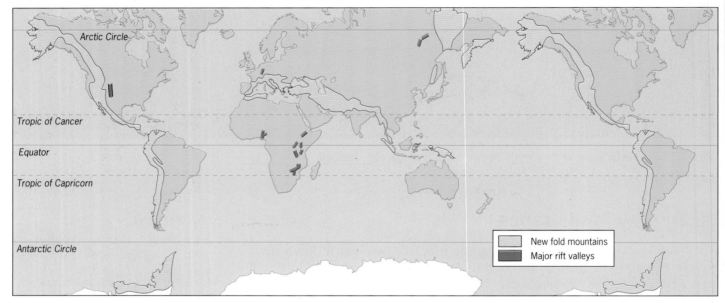

Fig. 2.34 World distribution of fold mountains and rift valleys.

EXERCISES

14a Using an atlas and Figure 2.34, identify the major fold mountain ranges in Asia, North America, South America and Europe.

b* Compare the distribution of fold mountains (Fig.2.34) with the boundaries of the main plates (Fig.1.7). Describe the similarities and suggest possible reasons for them.

Anticlines and synclines

If you put a sheet of A4 paper on a flat surface and apply gentle pressure from both ends, the paper will form a simple arch or upfold. In a similar way rocks are folded by powerful tectonic forces. We refer to these upfolds as **anticlines** (Fig.2.35).

In South-East England, the Weald in Kent and Sussex was originally a dome-shaped anticline (Fig.2.37). After the dome was formed, the forces of weathering and erosion got to work. Rivers stripped away the outermost layers of rock, so that today we are left with an eroded anticline. The covering of chalk, long since removed, forms the inward facing escarpments of the North and South Downs (Fig.2.31).

Sometimes, instead of pushing the rocks up, folding creates a downfold or **syncline** (Fig.2.35). Both London and Paris are located in the centre of basins or synclines.

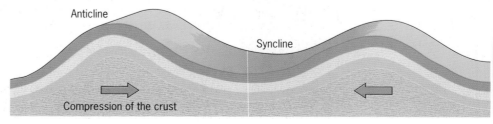

Fig. 2.35 An anticline and syncline.

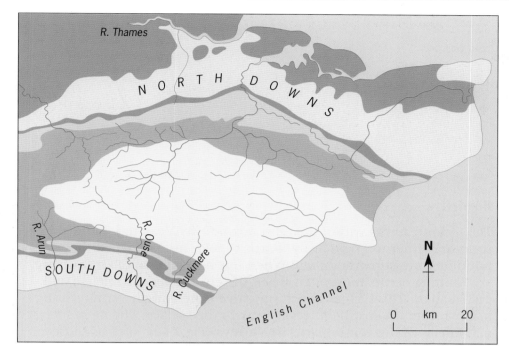

Fig. 2.36 The geology of the Weald.

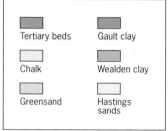

▨ Tertiary beds	▨ Gault clay
▢ Chalk	▨ Wealden clay
▨ Greensand	▢ Hastings sands

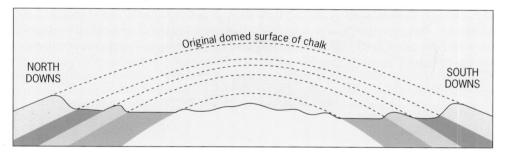

Fig. 2.37 A cross-section of the Weald, an eroded anticline.

To understand folding we must go back to the ideas of plate tectonics in Chapter 1. Imagine two continents, separated by a shallow sea, and moving together. As the continents get closer, the sedimentary rocks on the sea bed crumple upwards to form fold mountains. This is exactly how the Himalayas were formed as India was transported on the Indo-Australian plate northwards towards Eurasia (Fig.2.39). We know that the rocks which today form the Himalayas were once on the sea bed, because they contain the fossil remains of sea creatures.

Fig. 2.38 The Himalayas: fold mountains formed by the collision of India with Eurasia.

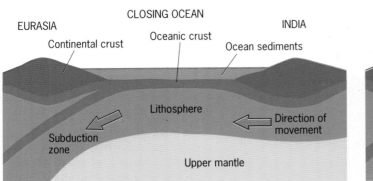

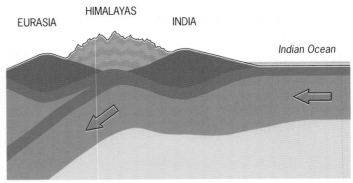

Fig. 2.39 The formation of the Himalayas.

Faulting

The tectonic forces within the crust don't always lead to folding. Some rocks are either too rigid or too brittle to fold. Instead, when they are put under pressure, they snap. When this happens we call it **faulting**.

Faulting occurs most often when the crust is being stretched and pulled apart. This happens at constructive plate margins, where rising magma from the mantle forces its way to the surface. The most spectacular effects of this tension are **rift valleys** (Fig.2.40), such as those found in the mid-ocean ridges, and the East African Rift Valley (Fig.2.42). Volcanic eruptions often take place when rift valleys are formed. Simpler types of faulting are normal faults, reverse faults and tear faults (Figs.2.41). Both normal and reverse faults can create steep slopes known as fault scarps.

EXERCISES

16a Study Figure 2.41 and explain the difference between a normal and a reverse fault.
b Use an atlas and Figure 2.34 to find the countries in which the following rift valleys are located: Rhine Rift Valley; Lake Baikal; East African Rift Valley; the Dead Sea.
c* Refer back to section 1.4 on earthquakes. Try to explain why faulting often causes earthquakes and earth tremors.

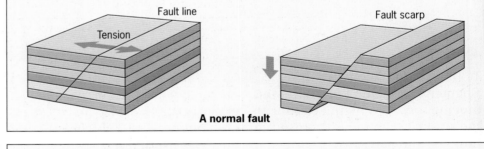

A normal fault

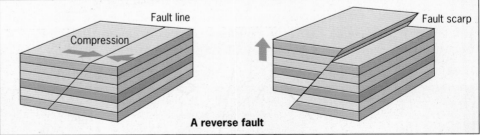

A reverse fault

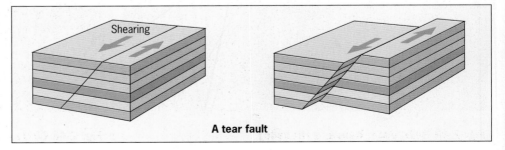

A tear fault

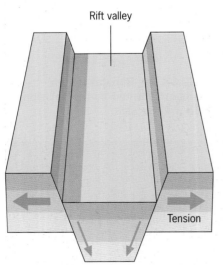

Fig. 2.40 The formation of a rift valley.

Fig. 2.41 Types of faults.

2.10 Summary: rocks and landscapes

Key ideas	Generalisations and detail
Rocks are made from a mixture of minerals.	• Granite is made up of quartz, feldspar and mica; limestone of calcium carbonate.
There are three main types of rock: igneous, sedimentary and metamorphic.	• Igneous rocks such as granite and basalt are formed from molten rock or magma. • Sedimentary rocks result either from the breakdown of pre-existing rocks (e.g. sandstone) or from the build up of plant and animal remains on the sea floor (e.g. limestone). • Metamorphic rocks (e.g. slate and marble) have been altered by great heat and/or pressure.
Rocks have a structure.	• Rocks contain lines of weakness such as joints and bedding planes. Sedimentary rocks were deposited in layers or strata.
Rocks are changed by the process of weathering.	• Physical weathering by frost or the sun breaks down rocks into smaller fragments. • Chemical weathering destroys rocks by altering their mineral composition.
Some rocks produce distinctive landscapes.	• Granite often produces upland landscapes (e.g. Cairngorm plateau) with features such as tors, blockfields and screes. Land use is mainly restricted to rough grazing and recreation. • Minor igneous intrusions, such as sills and dykes, form important local features such as vertical scars and waterfalls. • Limestone produces upland landscapes known as karst. They include pavements, scars, dry valleys, shake holes, caves and caverns. Soils are thin and not suitable for farming, though recreation is often important. • Chalk is associated with gentle uplands or escarpments. These consist of a steep scarp slope and a gentle dip slope. There is little surface drainage today. • Clay gives rise to gentle lowland landscapes of great value to agriculture.
Rocks have great economic value.	• Hard rocks such as dolerite and granite may be used as roadstone. Clay baked into bricks is a valuable building material, and so is sandstone. Limestone is a vital raw material used in the chemical, steel and agricultural industries. Weathered granite forms china clay which is used for pottery manufacture (Fig. 2.43).
Rock structure and scenery is influenced by folding and faulting.	• Pressure caused by plate movements produces simple upfolds or anticlines (e.g. the Weald) and downfolds or synclines (e.g. the London Basin), as well as major fold mountain ranges, such as the Himalayas. When rocks fracture instead of folding, they form rift valleys (e.g. Jordan valley) and fault scarps.

Fig. 2.42 Hell's Gate, Kenya, a rift valley.

Fig. 2.43 China clay quarry, Cornwall.

3 Weather and climate

EXERCISES

1a Study Figures 3.1–3.6 and suggest ways in which the type of weather shown might affect human activities.
b Search the newspapers (in your local or school library) for articles concerning weather. Why did the weather make the news? Was its impact good or bad?

3.1 Introduction

For British people, the weather is an endless topic of conversation. More often than not we complain about our weather: it's either too cold or too wet, or more rarely too hot or too dry. Neither do we trust our climate. Every year millions of Britons go to the Mediterranean, because they expect the summer at home to be cool and damp.

In this chapter we begin by focusing on the features of weather and climate, then on the climate of the British Isles. Finally we study extreme weather events such as tropical storms and droughts. However, we need to be clear about the difference between weather and climate.

Fig. 3.1-3.6 Many different types of weather.

3.2 What are weather and climate?

Weather and climate are about the same things: temperature, rainfall, wind speed, sunshine, the amount of cloud and so on. And yet weather and climate are not the same. The difference is one of time scale. Weather is about the short term: what's going to happen to temperature and **precipitation** (rain, snow, sleet etc.) today or tomorrow. Climate involves longer time-scales. It is the seasonal pattern of weather we can expect on the basis of past experience. We could say that climate is only weather averaged out over 30 or more years.

In many parts of the world the climate has a definite pattern. For example, at the Equator almost every day is hot and sunny with heavy rainfall in the late afternoon. In much of tropical Africa and South Asia, summers are wet and winters are dry. In the Mediterranean it is the other way round. But in the British Isles it is not nearly so simple. Someone once said that in the British Isles there was no climate, only weather. For example, as I write this, it is late April and it's snowing hard, but a week ago the temperature touched 20°C.

Table 3.1 Average daily maximum temperatures at London

Month	°C	Month	°C
January	6	July	22
February	7	August	21
March	10	September	19
April	13	October	14
May	17	November	10
June	20	December	7

3.3 The global climate

Large parts of the world have similar patterns of temperature and precipitation. This enables us to recognise climate regions (Fig 3.7).

Fig. 3.7 World climate regions

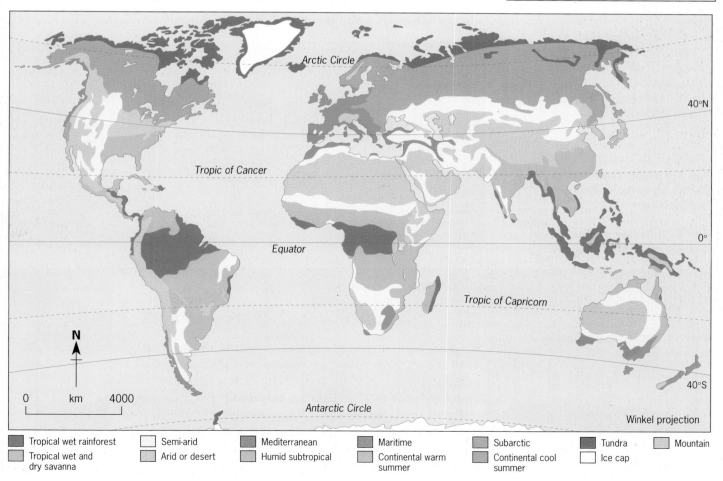

Tropical wet rainforest — Semi-arid — Mediterranean — Maritime — Subarctic — Tundra — Mountain
Tropical wet and dry savanna — Arid or desert — Humid subtropical — Continental warm summer — Continental cool summer — Ice cap

EXERCISES

2a Using the daily weather report in a national newspaper, keep a record of London's maximum temperatures for a week.
b How do the week's temperatures compare with the climatic average in Table 3.1?
c* Explain why it is unlikely that your week's record will match the monthly average temperature exactly.

EXERCISES

3 Study Figure 3.7. What type of climate does the British Isles have?
Which other countries have a similar climate?

EXERCISES

Study figure 3.9.

4 Along which line of latitude is the sun overhead on the 21st June and the 21st December? What season of the year is it in Britain?

5 Explain why the South Pole is warmer than the North Pole on the 21st December.

6* Imagine an area of land extending from the Equator to the North Pole. Draw this continent and mark on it the following lines of latitude: Equator, tropics, polar circles. Draw in the areas which would have equatorial, tropical, temperate and polar climates if latitude was the only influence on the climate.

Fig. 3.8 (above right) The effect of latitude on temperature.

EXERCISES

7 Study Figures 3.9 and 3.10. Suggest why the area inside the Arctic Circle is often called the 'land of the midnight sun'.

Fig. 3.9 (right) The effect of the Earth's tilt in the northern hemisphere.

Fig. 3.10 (below) The pattern of daylight in an Arctic summer.

Latitude and climate

At the global scale latitude is the biggest influence on climate. This is because the sun's angle changes with latitude and with it the amount of heat energy received at the Earth's surface. The simple rule is that the higher the sun is in the sky, the more concentrated are its rays, and the higher the temperature. Figure 3.8 shows how this happens.

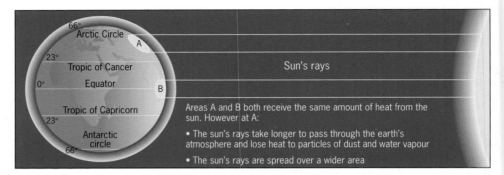

Areas A and B both receive the same amount of heat from the sun. However at A:

• The sun's rays take longer to pass through the earth's atmosphere and lose heat to particles of dust and water vapour

• The sun's rays are spread over a wider area

Latitude also affects temperature by influencing day length. (See Fig. 3.9) The length of day does not vary much in the tropics but as latitude increases it becomes more important. In the British Isles in winter, days are short and nights are long, and this contributes to low temperatures. Further north, inside the Arctic Circle (66.5°N) the winter days become so short that for several weeks the sun does not rise at all. However, in summer there is a similar period with 24 hours of daylight.

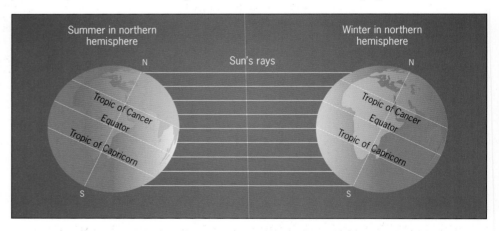

Table 3.5 The effects of relief and longitude on precipitation in the British Isles

	West	East
Upland	1500 – 5000 mm *Brecon Beacons*	1000 – 2000 mm
Lowland	900 – 1500 mm	600– 900 mm

EXERCISES

13 Use an atlas to locate the following regions: Dartmoor, Brecon Beacons, Lake District, Snowdonia, Cheviots, Cairngorms, North West Highlands, Vale of York, East Anglia, Fens, Thames Estuary, Fylde, Solway Lowlands, Somerset Levels, Anglesey and North York Moors. Then copy Table 3.5 and allocate each region to one of the four precipitation categories as in the example for the Brecon Beacons.

In the British Isles mean annual precipitation is high and spread throughout the year. This is unlike the Mediterranean, where there is a wet and a dry season.

High precipitation in the British Isles is easily explained. The prevailing westerly winds pick up moisture from the ocean and, as they sweep in from the Atlantic, the British Isles are the first obstacle in their path. When this moist air hits the western mountains, it sheds large amounts of precipitation. We call this relief or **orographic** precipitation (Fig. 3.22).

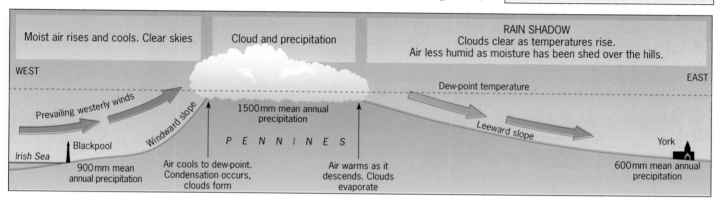

In the lowlands there is less precipitation , and amounts decrease eastwards. In part this is because so much moisture has been 'spent' in the uplands. However, this is not the whole story: as the moist air descends from the mountains, it warms up and the moisture evaporates reducing precipitation and creating a **rain shadow** (Fig. 3.22). Many parts of eastern England and eastern Scotland lie in a rain shadow.

Most precipitation in the British Isles comes from mid-latitude storms

Fig. 3.22 (above) Relief precipitation and the rain shadow effect in northern England.

Fig. 3.23 (left) Mean annual precipitation for southern England.

Fig. 3.24 (below) Relief cross section from Wales to southern England.

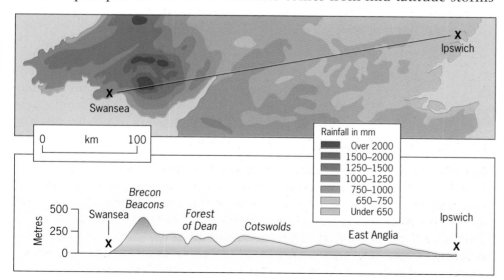

EXERCISES

14 Study Figures 3.23 and 3.24.
a Trace Figure 3.24.
b Draw a section along line X–X (Fig. 3.23) to show precipitation between Swansea and Ipswich. Use a vertical scale of one centimetre to 1000 mm of precipitation for your section.
c Name the areas of highest and lowest precipitation and describe the effect of relief on precipitation.
d* Explain the changes in precipitation along the section.

known as depressions (see section 3.9). However, in eastern England thunderstorms also contribute significant amounts of **convectional** precipitation, especially in summer (fig.3.26). In summer the sun heats the ground, causing the warm air to rise in a column or convection current. As the air rises, it cools until it forms towering thunderstorm (cumulo-nimbus) clouds (Fig.3.25). Because of their great thickness, these clouds completely blot out the sun and often produce lightning, thunder and very heavy showers of rain and hail.

Fig. 3.25 (above) A cumulo-nimbus cloud.

Fig. 3.26 (right) Convectional precipitation and thunderstorms.

Fig. 3.27 (below) Understanding weather charts.

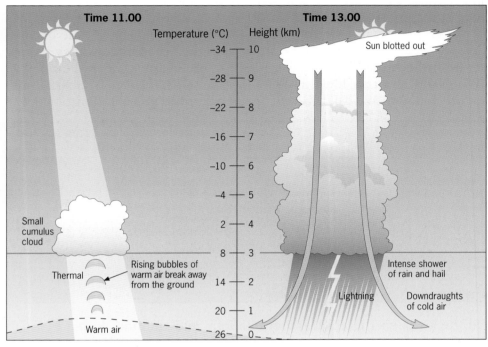

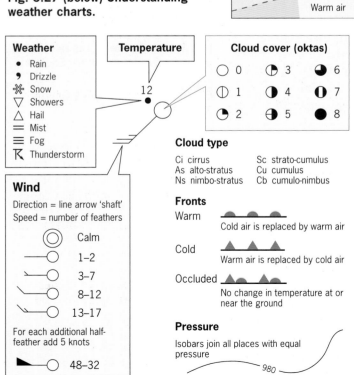

3.8 Weather charts

If you look at the weather forecast on television or in newspapers you will see weather charts (Fig.3.28). The most important feature on these charts are **isobars** – lines joining places of equal pressure. Circular patterns of isobars pick out areas of low pressure (**depressions**) and high pressure (**anticyclones**). Sometimes the isobars are packed closely together. This indicates strong winds. When the isobars are spaced widely apart, they show light winds or calm conditions. Isobars on maps can also help us to tell the wind direction, because surface winds blow from areas of high pressure to areas of low pressure.

Weather charts also provide information about the weather, especially temperature, cloud cover and precipitation (Fig.3.27). This information is given as a series of symbols for each weather station (Fig.3.29).

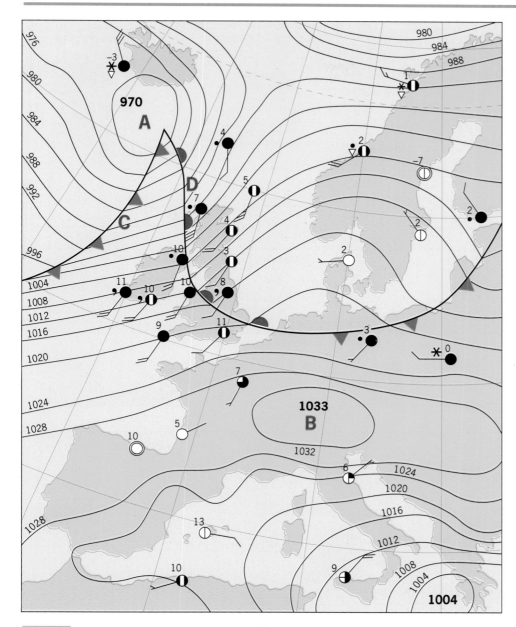

Fig. 3.28 (left) Weather chart for 15.1.95.

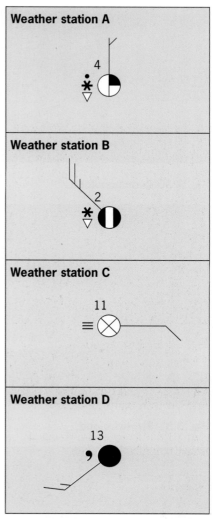

Weather station A

Weather station B

Weather station C

Weather station D

Fig. 3.29 (above) Weather station plotting models.

3.9 Depressions and anticyclones

Air masses are large bodies of air with distinct characteristics of temperature and humidity. Several different air masses meet over the British Isles, some originating in the tropics and others in the arctic. The meeting of these different air masses is responsible for the changeable weather of the British Isles. On most days the weather charts for the British Isles and the North Atlantic are dominated either by depressions or anticyclones. Depressions are large areas of low pressure. They form over northern Canada and the Atlantic Ocean where warm tropical air meets cold polar air. They may be up to 2 000 kilometres in diameter. Normally they move rapidly eastwards, often crossing the Atlantic in just two or three days. On three days out of four, depressions are responsible for our weather. They bring typically mild, wet and stormy conditions, followed by brief intervals of bright, sunny weather.

EXERCISES

15 Study Figure 3.27 and then describe the weather conditions at each station in Figure 3.29.

Fig. 3.30 Cumulus cloud.

Fig. 3.31 Stratus cloud.

Fig. 3.32 Cirrus clouds.

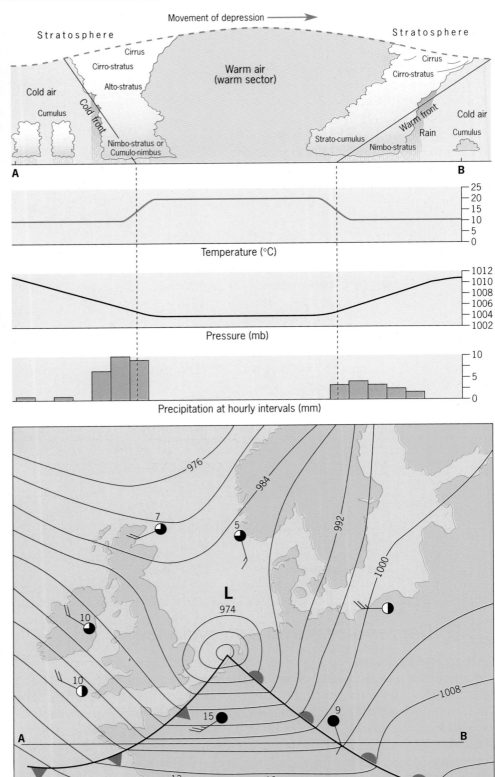

Fig. 3.33 Weather conditions in a depression.

The cause of the wet and cloudy weather in depressions is clear from Figure 3.33. In depressions, air rises along **fronts** where warm and cold air meet. Warm air is confined to a wedge-shaped area known as the warm sector (Fig.3.33). The warm air gradually slides above the cold air. We already know that when air rises it cools, and forms clouds and precipitation. Thus the warm and cold fronts in depressions are marked by great swirls of thick rain-bearing clouds (Fig.3.35). Eventually the warm air is undercut by the faster moving cold air and lifted off the ground. It is then called an occluded front

In many respects anticyclones (Fig.3.34) are the exact opposite of depressions (Table 3.6). Often they bring extreme temperatures. In summer, temperatures may rise into the mid-20s and above, while in winter, cold and frosty weather is common. However, the most difficult aspect of anticyclonic weather to predict is sunshine. Winter anticyclones may be either clear and bright, or overcast with extensive low cloud and fog. The sun may be hidden behind a cloud blanket for several days. People call such weather 'anticyclonic gloom'.

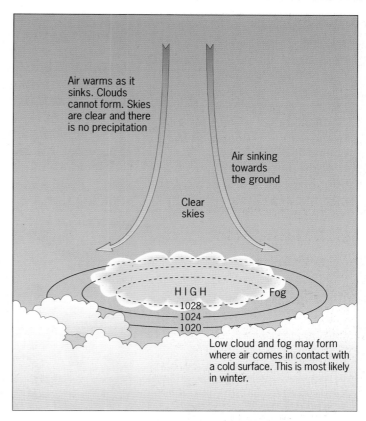

Fig. 3.34 An anticyclone.

Table 3.6   Comparison of depressions and anticyclones

	Depressions	Anticyclones
Pressure	Low	High
Winds	Strong	Light
Wind circulation	Anticlockwise	Clockwise
Precipitation	Steady at the warm front Heavy showers at the cold front	Usually none
Air masses	Two: warm and cold separated by fronts	One: there are no fronts

Table 3.7 The weather pattern in a depression

	As warm front approaches	In the warm sector	As the cold front approaches	Behind the cold front
Temperature				
Pressure				
Wind direction				
Cloud				
Precipitation				

3.10 Satellite images

Since the 1960s weather forecasters have relied on satellite images of clouds as well as weather charts. A number of satellites dedicated to weather forecasting transmit both visible and infra-red images. Visible images record the earth's atmosphere and surface as we would see them from space.

EXERCISES

16* Study Figure 3.33. Then copy Table 3.7 and fill it in to describe how temperature, pressure, wind direction, cloud and precipitation change as a depression moves across an area.

EXERCISES

17 Study the weather chart in Figure 3.28.
a Name features A and B.
b Name fronts C and D.
c Why are the winds stronger at C than at D?
d Describe the weather conditions in the south and north of the British Isles.
e* Why is it warmer in Ireland than in north-east England?
f* Describe how the weather in Scotland is likely to change in the next 24 hours.

EXERCISES

18a Trace the outline of Europe and the main cloud masses from the satellite image (Fig.3.35). With reference to Figure 3.28, label the areas of cloud along the warm and cold fronts, and the shower cloud behind the cold front.

b Mark on your tracing the position of the warm and cold fronts and likely areas of precipitation.

c* What does Figure 3.35 tell you about the temperature and height of the main cloud bands?

19a Describe the differences in temperature between the Mediterranean Sea, and the land masses of Spain and southern France.

b* Try to explain the differences by looking back at section 3.3. How and why would you expect the pattern of temperature in these areas to differ in July?

Satellite images are easy to understand: the more a surface reflects light, the brighter it appears on a visible image. Thus thick clouds and ice sheets are white, while seas and oceans are black.

Infra-red images (Fig.3.35) tell us about the temperature of clouds and the earth's surface. The darker the surface, the warmer it is. This information is useful to weather forecasters, because it tells them about the height of clouds, and the temperatures of land and sea surfaces.

Depressions often form striking images when seen from space (Fig.3.35). The fronts are picked out by great swirling bands of rain-laden cloud, like a giant Catherine wheel. Behind the fronts, shower clouds have a mottled appearance, with each individual cumulus cloud standing out as a tiny parcel.

Fig. 3.35 (right) A satellite image of a depression, 15.01.95.

Table 3.8 Interpreting visible light and infra-red images

Tone	Visible	Infra-red
Black	Surfaces which absorb light e.g. oceans, seas lakes.	Warm/hot surfaces e.g. tropical oceans hot deserts.
Grey	Moderately absorptive surfaces e.g. vegetation, crops	Moderate temperatures: low clouds; western Europe in winter.
White	Highly reflective surfaces e.g.snow, ice, thick cloud, deserts.	Cool/cold surfaces: land and sea in high latitudes; high clouds.

3.11 Weather hazards

Tropical cyclones

Tropical cyclones is the name given in South Asia to violent storms which are generated over warm tropical oceans. In the Caribbean and USA the same storms are called hurricanes, while in East Asia and South-East Asia they are known as typhoons.

Tropical cyclones are rather like stronger versions of mid-latitude depressions. They are areas of intense low pressure, around which very strong winds, cloud and heavy rain rotate (Fig.3.37). Wind speeds commonly exceed 150 km/h and can cause immense damage (Table 3.9). Over the sea, the winds pile up the water into enormous waves or surges which often flood low-lying coastal areas.

Cyclones usually develop over the oceans in late summer and early autumn when the surface water is at its warmest (at least 27°C). At these temperatures water rapidly evaporates. The rising air cools and, as it condenses, releases huge amounts of heat. This heat provides the energy to power these tropical storms. However, once over a land mass, and deprived of their energy supply, tropical cyclones quickly blow themselves out.

Table 3.9 Major cyclone disasters

Date	Deaths	Location
1780	20 000	West Indies
1881	300 000	East China-Vietnam
1900	6 000	Galveston, Texas
1935	800	Florida Keys
1970	450 000	Bangladesh
1990	28	Caribbean, N and S Carolina
1991	125 000	Bangladesh
1992	22	Florida

Fig. 3.36 (left) A satellite image of hurricane Andrew over the Gulf of Mexico.

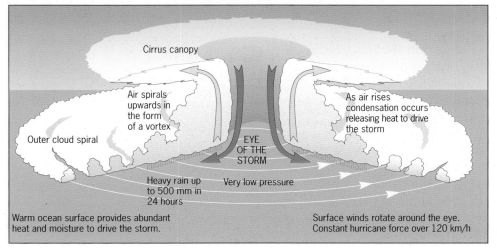

Cirrus canopy

Air spirals upwards in the form of a vortex

As air rises condensation occurs releasing heat to drive the storm

Outer cloud spiral

EYE OF THE STORM

Heavy rain up to 500 mm in 24 hours

Very low pressure

Warm ocean surface provides abundant heat and moisture to drive the storm.

Surface winds rotate around the eye. Constant hurricane force over 120 km/h

Fig. 3.37 (below) Cross-section through a tropical cyclone.

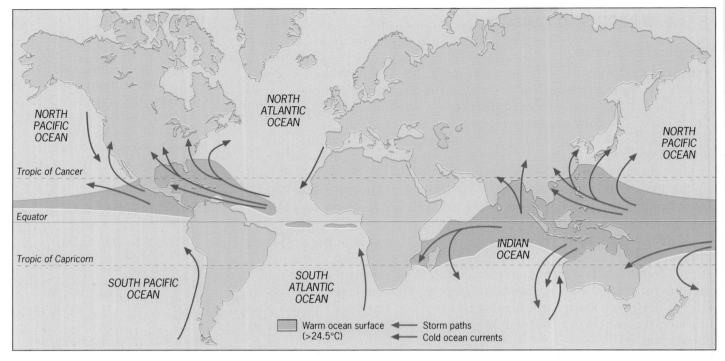

Fig. 3.38 Regions where tropical cyclones develop.

3.12 The 1991 Bangladesh cyclone disaster

Bangladesh is one of the world's most densely populated countries. Its population –122 million, nine-tenths of whom live in the countryside – is supported on an area barely half the size of the UK. It is also one of the world's poorest countries.

Situated at the head of the Bay of Bengal, most of Bangladesh is a **delta** formed by the convergence of three great rivers – the Ganges, the.Brahmaputra and the Meghna (Fig.3.39). Eighty per cent of Bangladesh is less than 1.5 metres above sea level, and every year during the wet (monsoon) season the rivers flood half the country to a depth of 30 cm. The floods, which last for several months bring fertile silt, but cause great disruption. Yet these annual floods are insignificant compared to the really disastrous floods caused by tropical cyclones. In 1970 a tropical cyclone and tidal surge killed more than 450 000 people.

A repeat of this disaster occurred in 1991 (Fig.3.39) when a cyclone hit the south-east coast and delta. A 7m-high tidal wave, whipped up by winds of over 200 km/h, killed 125 000 people.

Diary of a disaster

30 April, 1991
Shortages of food and safe drinking water already face survivors in the south-east of Bangladesh.

2 May
There is a serious risk of cholera and other diseases. Lack of hygiene and water supplies contaminated by sewage and dead bodies spread the fear of epidemics. Famine and starvation are a threat in remote areas without road links. The government is hampered in its relief effort by a lack of helicopters and appeals for international aid.

6 May
Food shortages are more widespread. 4 million survivors face starvation and disease. Lack of food is serious because the cyclone struck just before the harvest when food reserves were already low.

7 May
The government asks the world community for $1.4bn. $200bn of aid is pledged by Saudi Arabia, the European Community, the United Kingdom, Germany, France, Italy, Canada and Japan.

9 May
The Red Cross and the government step up relief efforts. Diarrhoea and dysentery affect thousands of children in the islands and in the south-east.

"The whole sky turned black and cold winds started to blow. There was such a roar, I thought my eardrums would burst. Somehow I survived the night clinging to a tree. In the morning I returned home to find my father weeping. My brother and sister were dead." (Khairal Amin, survivor of the 1991 cyclone disaster)

Apart from the loss of life, crops, livestock, roads, bridges and electricity pylons were destroyed (Fig.3.39). Salt water contaminated farm land, and drinking water supplies were polluted. The Bangladesh government estimated the damage at US$ 1.5 billion. The cyclone's main impact was felt along the south-east coast and in remote islands, such as Sandvip and Hatia in the delta, where evacuation was impossible (Fig.3.40).

EXERCISES

21 Imagine that you are a journalist covering the Bangladesh cyclone disaster. Write a short article entitled 'countdown to a disaster' explaining the background to the disaster. Suggest what might be done to avoid a similar disaster in future.

Fig. 3.39 After the cyclone.

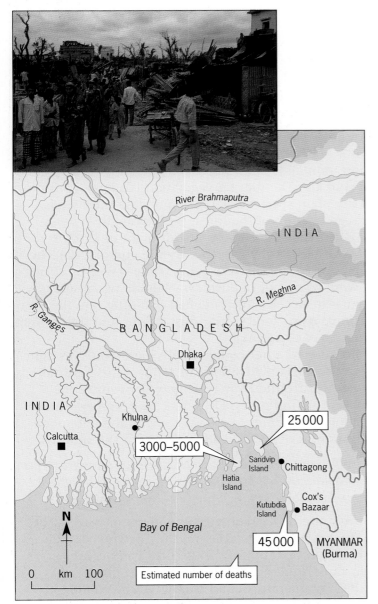

Fig. 3.40 Bangladesh after the flood.

Where natural disasters hit hardest

In 1992 hurricane Andrew devastated the coast of Florida in the USA (Fig. 3.36). It was one of the most powerful storms on record, and yet it killed fewer than 30 people. Why do natural hazards like cyclones hit poor countries so much harder?

The simple answer is poverty. Two-thirds of the people in Bangladesh live below the World Health Organisation's poverty line; half the rural population does not get enough to eat; and most rural dwellers are landless. Desperate people settle anywhere – even on temporary silt islands that emerge each year after the floods.

Monpura Island appeared suddenly when the Meghna River deposited silt in its shifting channel. Belonging to no one, it was quickly settled by farmers . Its fertile soils promised good harvests of rice, string beans and water melons. But at a price.

Rahim Sarkar is a rice farmer on Monpura Island who lost his wife and three children in the 1991 cyclone. Landless, he had settled on the island with his family three years earlier, after being driven out by his landlord from his smallholding on the mainland. Mr Sarkar had known the risk he was taking. Monpura Island is extremely vulnerable. It lies directly in the path of cyclones. It is barely above sea level and its remoteness makes evacuation impossible. Mr Sarkar's house was a straw hut built on a raised mud platform which gave no protection. Yet along with the 7 million other   people who live on this disaster coast, poverty had left him no choice.

Loss of life was also high because of government incompetence. Between 1970 and 1991 the government built a mere 137 cyclone shelters. These few saved many lives but sadly thousands of poor people, unable to afford radios, were unaware of the danger from the approaching cyclone.

3.13 Drought and bush fires in Australia

Natural disasters don't just happen in economically developing countries. In Chapter 1 we saw how in Japan – one of the world's richest countries – the city of Kobe was devastated by an earthquake. In 1993 and 1994, much of Australia was hit by one of the worst droughts in this century. This triggered hundreds of bush fires in the east of the country.

Australia is by far the driest continent. Two-thirds of the country is either desert or semi-desert, and in some parts of the interior there may be no rain for several years (Fig.3.41).

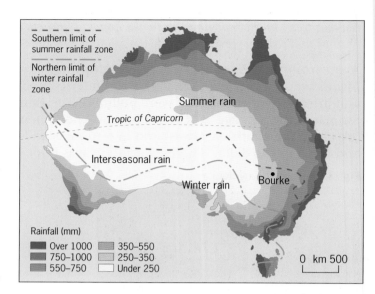

Fig. 3.41 (right) The distribution of precipitation in Australia.

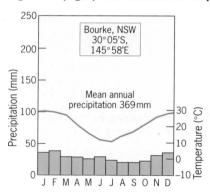

Fig. 3.42 Climate graph, Bourke.

EXERCISES

22 Compare the climate at Bourke in New South Wales (Fig.3.42) with Narvik in Norway (Fig.3.14). Suggest three reasons why drought is more likely to occur at Bourke.

Fig. 3.43 Bush fire – Sydney suburb.

Only the northern and eastern rims have more than 700 mm precipitation a year, and most areas have prolonged dry seasons. During the dry season, the heat causes billabongs (small lakes) and rivers to dry up. As a further complication, rainfall is often unreliable, making droughts and bush fires a harsh fact of life. The natural vegetation is adapted both to drought and fire. Many plant species need fire to release their seeds, and after bush fires regeneration of the forest occurs rapidly.

And yet, despite Australia's dry climate, the drought of 1993-4 seems to have caught Australians by surprise. By the end of 1994, the numbers of sheep had halved, topsoil was being blown away by strong winds, and farmers were going out of business. Wildlife was also badly affected, and some parts of eastern Australia had had little rain for over a year. Water restrictions, rising food prices, dust storms and soil erosion were direct consequences of the drought.

Long periods of hot, dry weather coupled with high winds brought the hazard of bush fires to eastern Australia. In January 1994, hundreds of fires raged out of control around Sydney. Ninety per cent of the Royal National Park went up in flames. Fires, reaching temperatures of 800°C, destroyed schools and homes; road, rail, power and telephone lines were cut and thousands of people had to flee from the suburbs.

Motorists panicked in traffic jams trying to get to their homes or away from them. The sun glowed through a mustard-coloured sky, and the stench of woodsmoke polluted the city (Sydney), home to 3.5 million people. The Sunday Times 9.1.94

During the worst period, there were more than 150 major blazes. The fires occurred from Queensland to Victoria and they destroyed 1.25 million acres of bush (Figure 3.43). Most of the fires were caused deliberately, but their rapid spread and large extent was due to the months of drought, high temperatures and strong winds. Wildlife in nature reserves was ravaged. Numbers of wallabies, possum, emus, kookaburras and other distinctive Australian animals were killed. The fires also wiped out many of the last remaining colonies of the koala.

3.14 Europe under water: the floods of January 1995

Towards the end of January 1995 there were severe floods in many parts of France, Belgium, the Netherlands and the UK. Rivers such as the Rhine and Maas rose to record levels. Over 250 000 people were evacuated when the Rhine threatened to burst through the dykes in the Netherlands (Fig.3.44), and in Belgium the floods were the worst for 60 years.

The main reason for the floods was the unusually high precipitation between November and January. In the UK, January 1995 was the fifth wettest month on record. During a normal winter we expect several spells of high pressure. These periods bring dry and quiet weather as the Atlantic storms are kept away from western Europe by the high pressure. In the winter of 1994-5 this didn't happen. Instead, a succession of storms brought heavy rainfall. By the end of January large areas of the lowlands of western Europe were flooded. There was enormous damage to property and some loss of life.

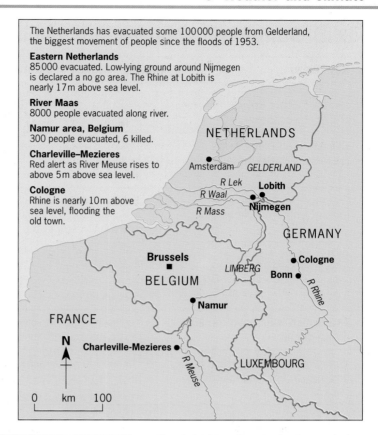

The Netherlands has evacuated some 100 000 people from Gelderland, the biggest movement of people since the floods of 1953.

Eastern Netherlands
85 000 evacuated. Low-lying ground around Nijmegen is declared a no go area. The Rhine at Lobith is nearly 17 m above sea level.

River Maas
8000 people evacuated along river.

Namur area, Belgium
300 people evacuated, 6 killed.

Charleville–Mezieres
Red alert as River Meuse rises to above 5 m above sea level.

Cologne
Rhine is nearly 10 m above sea level, flooding the old town.

Fig. 3.44 Flooding in the Low Countries: January 1995.

So who's to blame, then?

The water is up to the skirting boards, the dishwasher has shorted, the carpets are ruined and you never could afford the extra premiums the insurance company wanted against flooding. Who, if anyone, can be blamed for this fine mess?

How about fingering the usual suspects — governments? Politicians have pursued economic goals with startling ecological illiteracy for years; forests have been razed, watersheds mucked around with, hedges ripped out, ditches filled in and farmers encouraged to take land out of production. Fine, but all this leaves land more or less bare, which in turn means that water runs off hills or saturated earth into rivers faster than ever.

As rivers can't always cope, should we blame civil engineers? Since Victorian times they have argued that water should be drained from catchment areas as efficiently (ie, fast) as possible. Many billions of pounds have been spent raising river banks, canalising, channelling and diking almost everything that flows.

The Rhine alone has had 70 kilometres of meanders and bends straightened out; The Meuse, Waal and Lek proportionately fewer. But this means that these rivers now empty into Holland fuller and faster than ever before. If anything goes wrong, the damage is potentially worse than before. Mathematical models and historical data show that conditions which caused medium-scale floods in Victorian times would cause major floods today.

What about blaming metropolitan authorities? Just because you can't see many rivers or streams in towns doesn't mean they aren't there; in fact, they're mostly encased in concrete and taking more water than they ever used to straight into larger rivers or the sea. The more concrete and tarmac there is, the more rapid water run off there is. It now takes far less time for water to get from one end of the Rhine or the Thames to the other than it used to.

Planners and rural authorities might be kicked too, for allowing developers to build on land that always used to flood and farmers to claim land that rivers needed once a year. From Tewksbury to Delft, water meadows have been filled in, flood corridors have become prime sites for new roads, and low-lying farmland near towns has been taken over by supermarkets, housing and trading estates.

Fig. 3.45 An article from *The Guardian* 3.2.95.

EXERCISES

23 Although the winter of 1994-5 was exceptionally wet, the floods were not just caused by high rainfall. Read Figure 3.45 and explain how the following made flooding worse: deforestation; straightening the rivers' courses; urbanisation; planners.

3.15 Summary: Weather and climate

Key ideas	Generalisation and detail
Weather is the day-to-day state of the atmosphere .	• Weather in the British Isles and north-west Europe is very variable. In other parts of the world (e.g. around the equator) the weather is very constant.
Climate is the long-term (seasonal) pattern of weather.	• The main feature of climate is seasonal change in temperature and precipitation. Outside the tropics, climates have a warm and cold season. Within the tropics seasonal differences in precipitation (wet and dry seasons) are more significant.
Weather has an important impact on human activities.	• The disruptive effects of snow, ice and fog on transport movements. The effect on agriculture and water supply of summer droughts. Heavy precipitation and flooding from rivers in winter e.g. the floods in The Netherlands in January 1995.
At the global scale there are broad climate regions corresponding with belts of latitude.	• Latitude is the main influence on temperature. It determines the sun's angle in the sky and the amounts of solar radiation received by a place. From the equator to the poles climate changes from equatorial, to tropical continental, hot desert, Mediterranean, cool continental/maritime, cold continental, and polar.
The British Isles have a mild damp climate.	• The main influences on climate in the British Isles are: latitude, distance from the ocean, the North Atlantic Drift, the prevailing westerlies, altitude and aspect.
The climate of the British Isles has significant regional differences.	• The west is milder and wetter than the east; the south is warmer than the north. Highland Britain is both wetter and colder than Lowland Britain.
Precipitation – the moisture which falls from clouds.	• Precipitation includes rain, drizzle, snow, sleet and hail.
Precipitation occurs in three situations: when air is forced to cross mountains; in depressions along fronts; when air is heated and rises by convection.	• Precipitation in mountainous areas is called relief or orographic precipitation. It gives high precipitation in British uplands. Frontal precipitation occurs in depressions when air is forced to rise at warm and cold fronts. Most precipitation in the British Isles is frontal. Convectional precipitation follows intense heating of the ground by the sun. It causes showers and thunderstorms and is particularly important in the tropics.
Weather charts provide a daily summary.	• Weather charts summarize temperature, precipitation, cloud cover, wind direction/speed, pressure etc. These charts are essential for making forecasts. They are up-dated every six hours. The main features on these charts are isobars and fronts.
Depressions and anticyclones dominate Atlantic weather charts.	• Depressions are mid-latitude storms, bringing mild, wet, cloudy conditions to north-west Europe. • Anticyclones are areas of high pressure bringing, usually dry, settled weather. Temperatures are often extreme (cold in winter, warm in summer) with very variable amounts of sunshine.
Weather forecasters rely increasingly on satellite images.	• Both visible and infra-red images are used. They provide information on cloud patterns and temperature.
Tropical cyclones are violent storms which form over warm oceans.	• Tropical cyclones bring very strong winds and heavy rain. Every year they cause immense loss of life and damage to property in the tropics and sub-tropics.
Tropical cyclones hit poorer countries hardest.	• Hurricane Andrew (Florida 1992) was responsible for 22 deaths. The less powerful cyclone which struck Bangladesh in 1991 killed 125 000 people. Poverty, lack of early warning, lack of shelters and remoteness mean greater destruction in economically developing countries.
Climatic hazards can also have a severe impact on economically developed countries.	• The Australian drought and bush fires of 1993-4 devasted farming, forests, wildlife and many settlements in eastern Australia.

4 Ecosystems

4.1 Introduction

If you look at maps of the global distribution of climate, vegetation and soil in an atlas one feature stands out: their similarity. To a geographer this suggests that these three components are all closely related (Fig.4.1). The relationships between living things and their environment – **ecosystems,** are the focus of this chapter. We shall illustrate them with reference to one small-scale ecosystem – moorland, and three large-scale ecosystems: the tropical rainforest, the temperate deciduous forest, and the northern coniferous forest (Fig.4.2). We shall also consider the human impact on these ecosystems, which today is responsible for immense and far reaching changes.

Fig. 4.1 (right) The parts of an ecosystem.

Fig. 4.2 (below) World distribution of forest ecosystems.

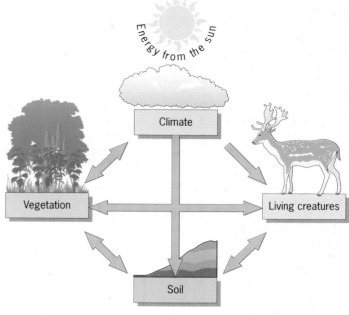

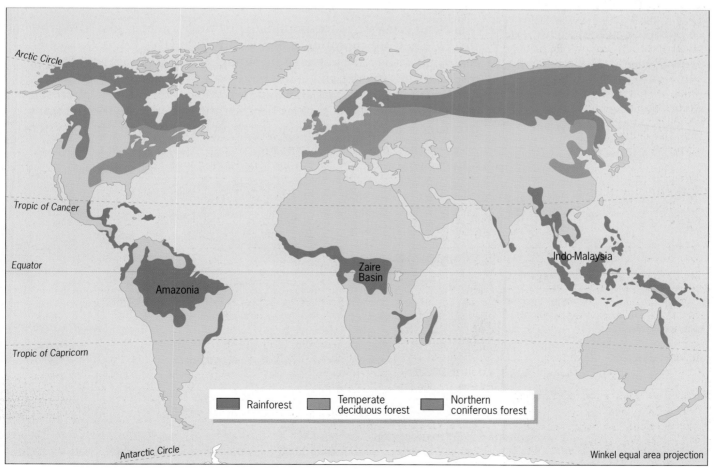

Fig 4.3 (left) Vegetation in the Mohave Desert, California.

Fig 4.4 (right) The tundra, Yukon, Canada.

EXERCISES

1a Study Figures 4.3 and 4.4. Identify the ecosystems shown using Figure 4.6 to help you.
b With reference to Figure 4.6 describe the climatic conditions which give rise to the vegetation in Figures 4.3 and 4.4.

Fig.4.5 A moorland ecosystem.

4.2 Local ecosystems: moorland

Ecosystems are groups of plants, animals and decomposers (such as fungi and bacteria) and their physical environment. Their main feature is that their various parts depend on each other. Plants, animals and decomposers are linked to each other, and to the physical environment, by complex flows of energy and cycles of matter.

Energy flows

Moorland ecosystems are dominated by herbs, grasses and low-growing shrubs. They are common in highland Britain (Figs.4.5, 4.7). Like all ecosystems, they are powered by sunlight. The green leaves of plants trap the sun's energy and combine it with CO_2, water and mineral nutrients to make sugars and starches. We call this process photosynthesis. Thus the plants such as heather and bilberry are the **primary producers**, and the basic food source for all animals in the ecosystem.

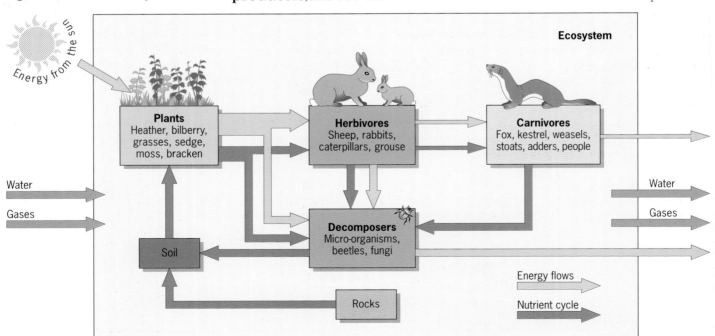

Some animals, such as caterpillars and rabbits, are herbivores which feed directly on the moorland plants. Others, such as insect-eating birds and foxes, feed on the herbivores, and are known as carnivores. In this way energy is transferred through the ecosystem in a **food chain** or **food web** (Fig.4.8). At each stage in the food chain there is less energy available. This is because plants and animals use energy in respiration, and in simply keeping alive.

Nutrient cycles

Ecosystems cycle mineral nutrients such as phosphorus, potassium, and calcium. Most mineral nutrients come from the weathering of rocks. Released into the soil they are taken up by the roots of plants and are transferred by herbivores and carnivores along food chains. Eventually all nutrients are returned to the soil when an organism dies. Here, dead plants and animals are broken down by fungi, bacteria and other decomposers. This makes them available for re-cycling. Without decomposers, ecosystems would quickly run out of mineral nutrients.

EXERCISES

2a Study Figure 4.8 and name a primary, secondary and tertiary producer.
b Why are plants so important in food webs?
c* What is likely to happen to the number and the size of organisms as you move along a food chain? Explain your answer.
d* Explain why animals at the end of the food chain are most at risk if the environment changes.

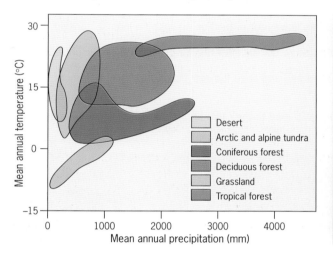

Fig. 4.6 (left) Relationship between climate and different ecosystems.

Food webs and nutrient cycles give ecosystems one of their key features: interpendence. What this means is that any change in one component in an ecosystem has a 'knock on' effect, causing change to occur elsewhere. Often these changes result from human interference. Invariably their impact is both unpredictable and damaging.

Fig. 4.7 (above right) Heather moorland in Swaledale, Yorkshire.

(Fig 4.8 (below left) A moorland food web.

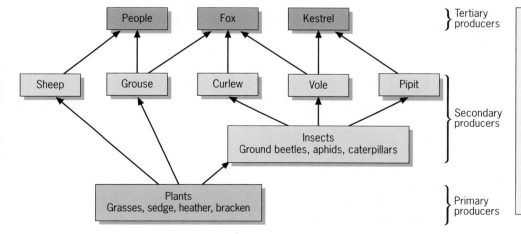

EXERCISES

3 Study the moorland ecosystem in Figure 4.5.
a How does energy enter the ecosystem?
b How does energy leave the system?
c What is the source of mineral nutrients?
d* Suggest how mineral nutrients could leave the system.

Fig. 4.9 The rainforest canopy, Guatemala.

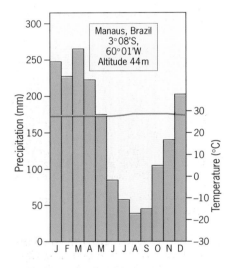

Fig. 4.10 Climate graph for Manaus,Brazil.

EXERCISES

4 Explain why temperatures at Manaus (Fig.4.10) are so constant throughout the year. Use Figure 3.8 to help you.

Fig. 4.11 The structure of a tropical rainforest.

4.3 Global ecosystems: tropical rainforests

The equatorial lowlands are home to the most productive and most diverse ecosystem on the planet: tropical rainforests. The rainforest covers nearly 17 million km², and is spread mainly across South America (Amazonia), central Africa (Zaire Basin), and South-East Asia (Indonesia and Malaysia) (Fig.4.2).

Tall forest trees dominate the rainforest. They absorb and use the sun's energy and control the environment for all other life forms. The equatorial climate has an enormous influence on rainforest vegetation (Table 4.1). Annual rainfall is high, ranging from 1500 to 4000 mm, and temperatures are constant, between 25°C and 30°C all year round (Fig.4.10). This gives ideal conditions for plant growth and helps to explain the huge **biomass** and biodiversity of the rainforest

Table 4.1 The influence of climate on the rainforest

- Trees are evergreen. High temperatures mean that there is no temperature limit to growth which continues throughout the year.

- Tall trees often have thick, leathery leaves for protection against the intense sunlight.

- Leaves have drip tips to shed moisture quickly after regular convectional downpours.

- Many trees are tall and shallow-rooted and need the extra support of buttress roots (Fig.4.14).

- High temperatures and high humidity lead to the rapid breakdown of dead plants and animals. Thus the cycling of nutrients takes place very quickly.

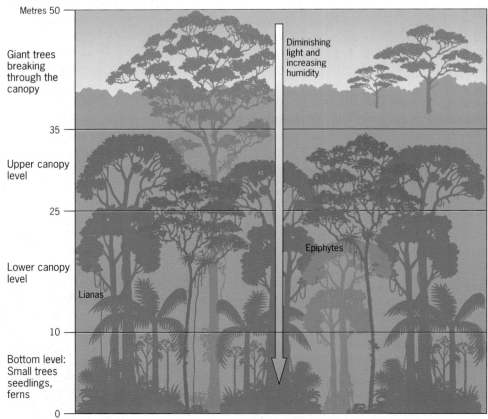

Forest layers

Like a city, with street-level activities, two- and three-storey apartment buildings, and soaring office towers, the rainforest has its own vertical structure (Fig.4.11). The topmost layer is the canopy. Viewed from above, the canopy is like a green ocean (Fig.4.9). Sunlight streaming down on the canopy, is converted into plant growth. This abundant food source attracts huge populations of insects, mammals and birds. Epiphytes, lianas and other climbing plants festoon the forest trees. Many have aerial roots and obtain their nutrients from rainwater.

Beneath the canopy, life is a struggle. The trees cast a dense shade, so that ground vegetation is sparse. Saplings may wait for years until a forest giant dies and leaves a gap in the canopy. Then, with a sudden burst of growth, they push towards the light.

Meanwhile, there is intense activity from fungi and micro-organisms on the forest floor, as they decompose and recycle the dead organic material. So efficient are they in this warm and humid environment that there is no thick layer of leaves on the forest floor.

Soils

Soils are a mixture of mineral and organic matter in which plants grow. The typical soils of the rainforest are deep and acidic (Fig.4.12). Their distinctive red colour comes from iron oxides. These build up in the top-most layers (horizons) of the soil.

It would seem logical that soils which support a dense vegetation would be highly fertile. In fact the reverse is true. Because the soils are old and have been weathered over long periods, they are low in essential nutrients like phosphate, potash and nitrate. Also, heavy rainfall quickly washes away any nutrients not taken up by the trees.

So with impoverished soils how does the rainforest survive? The secret is the rainforest's rapid nutrient cycle. Dead plant and animal remains which reach the forest floor are quickly broken down and the nutrients immediately absorbed by the trees. Thus the soil contains only a limited store of nutrients, which are mainly locked up in the trees. This has a lesson for farming. Destroy the trees and you remove the nutrients from the system, dooming permanent cultivation to failure.

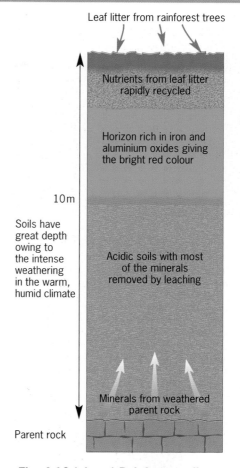

Leaf litter from rainforest trees

Nutrients from leaf litter rapidly recycled

Horizon rich in iron and aluminium oxides giving the bright red colour

10m

Soils have great depth owing to the intense weathering in the warm, humid climate

Acidic soils with most of the minerals removed by leaching

Minerals from weathered parent rock

Parent rock

Fig. 4.12 (above) Rainforest soil profile.

Fig. 4.13 (bottom left) The relationship between climate and diversity of vegetation in the northern hemisphere.

Fig. 4.14 (bottom right) Buttress roots on a rainforest tree.

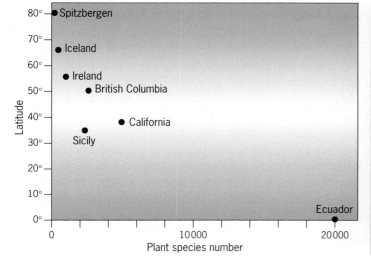

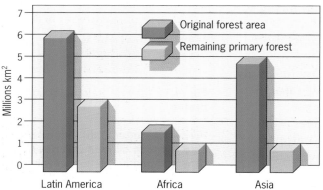

4.4 Amazonia

Amazonia is easily the largest area of rainforest on the planet (Fig.4.15). Although deforestation reduces it by around 15 000 km² a year, the rainforest still occupies an area eight times greater than the British Isles. On average, one hectare of rainforest supports up to 5000 trees and a mass of living matter (biomass) weighing more than 11 000 tonnes. So diverse is the plant and animal life in the rainforest that some scientists believe that nearly 90 per cent of all species are found there.

The rainforest also influences the climate in Amazonia. The trees act like giant pumps, taking water from the soil, and transpiring it through their leaves. This is a major cause of the heavy convectional rainfall (See 3.7) If the forest were destroyed, this water cycle would be broken and the region's climate would become much drier.

Deforestation: the crisis in Amazonia

The rainforest in Amazonia, like those in Africa and Asia, is under threat (Fig.4.16). Deforestation is taking place at an alarming rate. In Brazil, which covers the greatest part of Amazonia, only 60 per cent of the original forest remains. In Bolivia, the proportion is less than half. In total, an area of rainforest nearly twice the size of the British Isles has been destroyed since 1960. What is the cause of this destruction?

Fig. 4.15 (top) South America from space showing the River Amazon and the area of rainforest.

Fig. 4.16 (above) Destruction of the tropical rainforest.

The causes of deforestation

The main causes of deforestation in Brazil are population pressure and land hunger. Population growth has outstripped the government's ability to provide jobs for the people. Amazonia, with its vast empty spaces, huge timber and mineral resources, seemed to offer a solution to Brazil's economic problems.

Encouraged by the government and a major road-building programme (Figs. 4.18 and 4.19), migrants flooded into Amazonia, increasing its population from two to twenty million between 1960 and 1992. Most of the migrants were peasant farmers who were given small plots of rainforest by the government. The farmers tried to cultivate the land but this proved disastrous. They had to cope with poor soils, soil erosion, disease and insect pests. All this meant that most farmers were forced to abandon their plots after just three or four years of cultivation. Often their land was bought up by commercial cattle ranchers thus converting the richest ecosystem on earth into poor grazing land.

EXERCISES

Study Figure 4.16.
5a Which continent has the largest area of rainforest?
b Which continent has suffered the most deforestation?
c* Suggest reasons for the differences in rates of deforestation in Latin America, Africa and Asia.

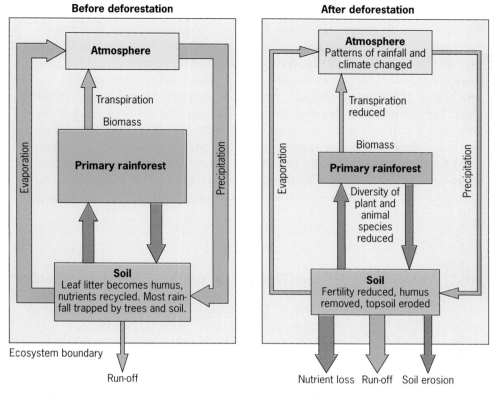

Before deforestation

Atmosphere

Transpiration

Biomass

Primary rainforest

Evaporation

Precipitation

Soil
Leaf litter becomes humus, nutrients recycled. Most rainfall trapped by trees and soil.

Ecosystem boundary

Run-off

After deforestation

Atmosphere
Patterns of rainfall and climate changed

Transpiration reduced

Biomass

Primary rainforest

Diversity of plant and animal species reduced

Evaporation

Precipitation

Soil
Fertility reduced, humus removed, topsoil eroded

Nutrient loss   Run-off   Soil erosion

Fig. 4.17 (above) The effect of deforestation on the ecosystem of the rainforest.

Fig.4.19 (below left) Roads and mineral reserves in the Brazilian Amazon.

Fig. 4.20 (below right) Poor grazing land in the Amazon following deforestation.

Fig. 4.18 A new road through the Amazon rainforest, Brazil.

EXERCISES
6 Study the changes to the rainforest ecosystem after deforestation (Fig.4.17).
a Describe the changes.
b* Explain the changes.

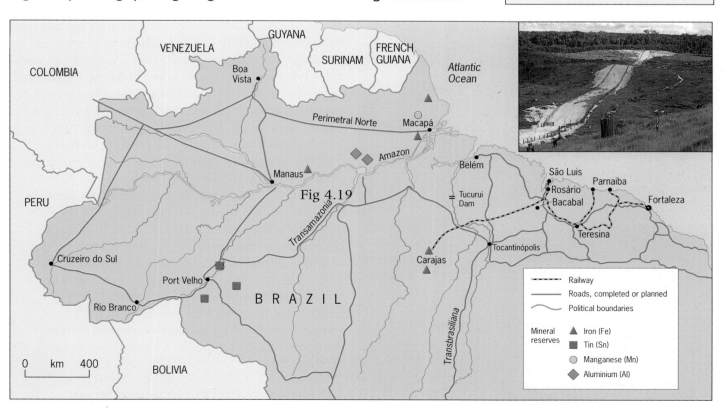

Fig. 4.21 Mining iron ore at Carajas.

Apart from the problem of population growth, Brazil also has a huge foreign debt. In order to pay off its debt, the government decided to develop Amazonia's fabulous mineral wealth. Its most ambitious scheme was at Carajas (Fig.4.19) in central eastern Amazonia. This area has rich mineral reserves of bauxite, gold, nickel and manganese, as well as the world's largest deposit of iron ore. Ore is shipped by rail to the Atlantic coast for export. The development of Carajas, the railway, and an iron smelting industry based on charcoal, meant that large areas of forest were destroyed. The harnessing of Amazonia's hydro-electric power (HEP) potential also caused large-scale forest destruction. When the huge dam at Tucurui was built to provide HEP for the aluminium smelting industry, thousands of square kilometres of rainforest were flooded.

CASE STUDY

4.22 (above) The location of Sarawak.

4.5 Logging in Sarawak: a chainsaw massacre

Sarawak, on the northern tip of the island of Borneo in South-East Asia, is about the same size as England, but has a population of only 1.5 million (Fig.4.22). Seventy per cent of Sarawak is still covered with primary rainforest and the timber industry is the biggest employer. Japan, North Korea and Taiwan are the main customers for the timber.

Most logging in the rainforest (Fig 4.23) does not involve clear felling (felling all trees over a wide area). This is because of the great diversity of the forest trees. Often there may be fewer than six commercially valuable hardwood trees per hectare. Unfortunately, for every tree that is extracted, five are badly damaged. Where tractors and bulldozers are used, further damage results from road-building and dragging timber along skid trails. Heavy machines churn up the soil, leaving the land ruined and causing erosion which silts up rivers.

Ideally, any logging operation should be sustainable. For example, if a hectare of forest grows one cubic metre of new wood in a year, then no more than this amount should be harvested annually. Today, Sarawak is harvesting more than twice as much timber as it should. At present rates of logging, Sarawak's rainforests will have completely disappeared by the year 2020.

If Sarawak's forests are to survive, production must be limited to sustainable levels. At the moment most exports are raw logs. If Sarawak could process or manufacture its timber (e.g. into veneers, plywood etc.) its exports would have added value, more jobs would be created, and fewer trees would have to be felled. Using helicopters to move logs would help to reduce unnecessary damage to non-commercial trees, though it is more expensive than conventional methods.

4.23 Forest destruction through logging, Sarawak.

EXERCISES

13a Draw three simple food chains for the coniferous forest with two, three and four levels in the chain.
b Study Figure 4.13 and describe how the number of plant species varies with latitude.
c* Suggest two reasons for this pattern.

EXERCISES

14* Make a table to compare the main features of rainforest, brown forest and podsol soils. Compare the soils under the following headings: depth, acidity, nutrient content, nutrient cycle, suitability for farming.

Most conifers are evergreens and, like the rainforest trees, do not lose their leaves once a year. Given the severe winters this may surprise you. Yet, there is a clear advantage for evergreens. They can begin to grow as soon as air temperatures rise above a daily average of 6°C. This gives them a head start over other species which have to use precious time growing new leaves every spring.

A second adaptation to climate is the conifers' needle-shaped leaves. These leaves have a thick outer skin and not many pores for transpiration. This reduces moisture loss which is essential because for much of the year water is frozen and is not available to plants. A third adaptation is the conical (Christmas-tree) shape of conifers which helps them to shed snow easily in winter.

Beneath the canopy of forest trees there is a layer of low-growing plants such as bilberry and cowberry, while lichens and mosses carpet the forest floor. Typical forest herbivores include insects, moose, beaver, squirrels and a variety of seed-eating birds. Carnivores include lynx, wolves, owls, pine martens and bears (which also eat plants).

Soils

The coniferous forest is based on shallow, acidic soils known as **podsols** (Fig.4.31). These soils are so infertile that cultivation is impossible. Conifer needles contain few nutrients. In the low temperatures they break down slowly and produce an acid humus. Rainwater filtering through the humus becomes highly acidic and washes nutrients from the soil's upper layer. This horizon becomes sandy and bleached. It is a distinctive feature of podsols (Fig.4.31). Some minerals and humus are deposited beneath this layer. Because podsols are so acid, they contain few earthworms which would normally mix the soil layers together. As a result these soils have very well developed and contrasting horizons. Podsol soils are also shallow due to the cold climate which slows down weathering processes as well as plant growth.

Fig. 4.31 Podsol soil profile.

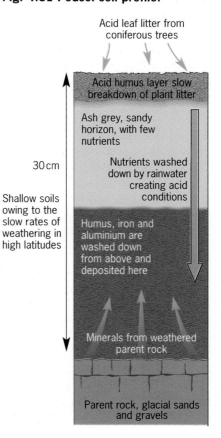

Acid leaf litter from coniferous trees

Acid humus layer slow breakdown of plant litter

Ash grey, sandy horizon, with few nutrients

Nutrients washed down by rainwater creating acid conditions

30 cm

Shallow soils owing to the slow rates of weathering in high latitudes

Humus, iron and aluminium are washed down from above and deposited here

Minerals from weathered parent rock

Parent rock, glacial sands and gravels

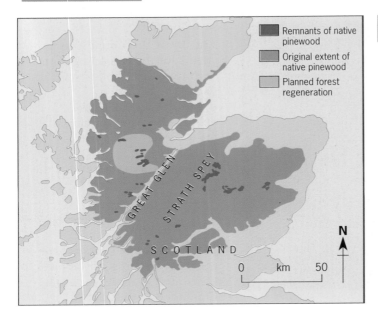

Fig. 4.32 (above) The Caledonian forest.

4.10 Caledon: the lost forest

Until the 18th century, large parts of the Highlands of Scotland were covered by a coniferous forest dominated by Scots pine. This was the ancient Caledonian forest: the western edge of the great coniferous forest which stretches across Eurasia. Today the Highlands are largely treeless. As the forest disappeared, most of the larger forest animals – beaver, moose, lynx, bear, wolf – disappeared too.

Human activity is responsible for the appearance of the Highlands today. Although deforestation has occurred since prehistoric times the main period of destruction was between about 1400 and 1800. Producing charcoal for iron making, clearing land for farming, and warfare between the English and Scots, completed the destruction of the forest. Since the 18th century, grazing by sheep and red deer has prevented the forest from regenerating.

EXERCISES

15 Imagine a public debate on a proposal to reafforest 1500 km² of mountain, moorland and rough pasture, and re-establish the original food web. The following people are represented in the debate: a conservationist; a landowner with shooting rights to deer and grouse; a hill sheep farmer; a representative of the Ramblers' Association; a local hotelier; and a member of the Scottish Tourist Board.
a In your role as one of these people set out your attitude to the proposal supporting your view with arguments. Be prepared to speak in a class debate.
b Summarise the viewpoints and arguments of the other interested parties in the debate.
c What is your personal opinion on the issue? What are the values and beliefs that led you to this opinion?

Fig. 4.33 Scots pines in Strathspey.

Today only a few tiny pockets of original forest survive in the Highlands (Fig.4.32). However, conservationists plan to re-establish large areas of the old Caledonian forest in the Highlands. Seeds taken from ancient pines (Fig.4.33) are used to raise saplings which are planted in specially fenced areas to protect them against deer. Meanwhile, foreign conifers are removed and replaced by native Scots pine and birch. The aim is to create a block of 1500 km² of natural forest. Once the forest is mature, it may be possible to re-introduce extinct forest animals, including bears and wolves, but this would be controversial .

4.11 Western Siberia: from wilderness to waste

Until the mid-1970s, the whole of western Siberia was an unspoilt ecosystem of lakes, bogs and immense pine and birch forests. The coniferous forest alone covered an area three times the size of the UK. Human activities were both sustainable and on a small scale. The semi-nomadic Selkup people herded reindeer, and the lakes and forests provided them with fish and furs.

But by the mid-1990s the situation had changed dramatically. Western Siberia now produced 60 per cent of Russia's oil. Also, huge amounts of natural gas were exported by pipeline to Western Europe. New cities grew up with great speed, among them Noyabr'sk, Surgut and Nizhnevartovsk (Fig.4.35).

Fig.4.34 Location of the oilfields.

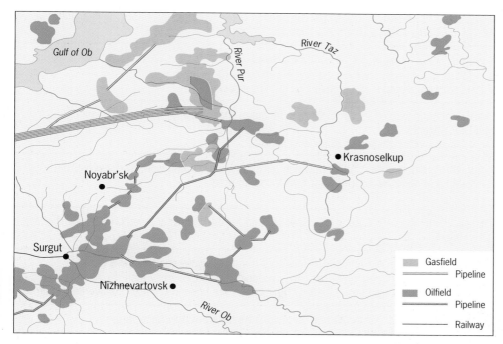

4.35 (left) Oil and gas in Western Siberia.

Unfortunately much of this development was unplanned and has been an environmental disaster. Millions of trees have been felled to make way for cities, roads, pipelines and electricity transmission lines. However, little of this timber has been collected and used. Large areas of forest have been destroyed by accidental fires. Road-building has disrupted the natural drainage, causing widespread flooding and further deforestation. Countless oil spills from rusty pipelines (Fig. 4.36) and careless drilling operations have polluted water supplies. More worrying, much of this pollution is being carried northwards towards the Arctic Ocean by rivers such as the Ob, Pur and Taz. There its effect could be even more devastating.

The coniferous forest ecosystem cannot easily recover from such damage. It is a fragile system. Nutrients are scarce, and cycle very slowly. It takes 150 years for trees, and almost as long for lichens, to reach maturity in this environment. Many scientists fear that it is already too late to save the environment in western Siberia.

4.36 Burning oil from a leaking pipeline.

71

4 Ecosystems

4.12 Summary: Ecosystems

Key ideas	Generalisations and detail
Ecosystems comprise plants, animals, decomposers and the physical environment.	• The living and non-living parts of ecosystems are linked together by a complex web of relationships. • Ecosystems are powered by sunlight. They have flows of nutrients. • Sunlight is trapped by plant leaves and converted to sugar and starch by photosynthesis. • Energy 'flows' through ecosystems along food chains and food webs.
Ecosystems vary in scale from local to global.	• Moorland is an example of a local ecosystem. The tropical rainforest, temperate deciduous forest and northern coniferous forest are global ecosystems.
The tropical rainforest is the most productive and most diverse ecosystem.	• The tropical rainforest is found in lowland areas within 10 degrees of the Equator and contains 90 per cent of all living species. • The rainforest climate is warm and humid. These conditions are ideal for plant growth.
The rainforest trees are adapted to the equatorial climate.	• Trees are evergreen (they don't lose their leaves once a year). Some trees have leathery leaves (with driptips) and buttress roots.
Rainforest soils have little fertility.	• Forest soils are acidic and contain few nutrients. • The forest is sustained by the rapid cycling of nutrients. • Permanent agriculture is not sustainable in the rainforest.
Exploitation of forest resources is rapidly destroying the rainforest.	• Deforestation is caused by agriculture, settlement, road building, mineral extraction, logging and HEP projects. • Most logging in the rainforest is not sustainable.
There are arguments for and against the destruction of the rainforest.	• Arguments centre on the conflict between environmentalists who want to conserve the rainforest and economists who want to develop its resources.
The temperate deciduous forest once covered most of Europe.	• The deciduous forest in Europe has been cleared for agriculture and settlement over the last 3000 years.
There are limits to plant growth in the temperate deciduous forest.	• Low winter temperatures reduce the length of the growing season to 8 or 9 months. • The temperate deciduous forest has lower productivity and diversity than the rainforest. • Trees are deciduous and broad leaved. Their leaves are shed in order to survive the winter.
Temperate deciduous forest soils favour agriculture	• The brown forest soils of the former deciduous forest are widely cultivated. • Brown forest soils are only slightly acid and have a rich store of nutrients.
There are attempts to re-establish the temperate deciduous forest in lowland Britain.	• A national forest is planned for the English Midlands, together with several smaller community forests.
The coniferous forest is found between the temperate deciduous forest and the Arctic.	• Climatic conditions set severe limits on plant growth in the coniferous forest. • Productivity and biodiversity in this type of forest are low.
Coniferous trees are adapted to the severe continental climate.	• Trees are evergreen and have needle-shaped leaves. • Trees have conical shapes.
The coniferous forest is the worlds main source of softwood and pulp.	• Canada, Sweden, Finland, Norway and Russia are the leading exporters of softwood timber and pulp.
Coniferous forest once covered the Highlands of Scotland.	• Attempts are being made to re-establish the ancient Caledonian forest in Scotland using seed from the trees in the remaining fragment of the original forest.

5 Settlement patterns

5.1 Introduction

We all know a lot about settlements. Whether sprawling cities or neat hamlets, settlements are where we live and where we spend most of our time. Settlements have many different purposes: they are places to work in, places to shop in, places to visit, and for all of us they are simply home. Most settlements have a long history – for instance, it is likely that people have occupied the settlement where you live for many centuries. The past is all around us – a village green laid-out in Anglo-Saxon times; a street pattern that was planned in the Middle Ages; a town hall built by the Victorians and so on. Without realising it our lives are influenced by settlements which have often been designed to meet the needs of an earlier age. In this chapter we try to answer basic questions about the location, size, shape and purpose of settlements.

EXERCISES

1 Study Figure 5.1. Draw a labelled sketch of Whalton to show the following features: buildings, roads, services (e.g. church) and open spaces.

Fig. 5.1 (below) An aerial photograph of Whalton.

EXERCISES

2a How old is the settlement in which you live? Find out by looking in a dictionary of place names in your school or local library and at old maps.
b* 'The past is all around us'. How well does this statement describe your journey to school?

EXERCISES

3a How does Whalton (Fig.5.1) compare with the settlement in which you live (size, density of building, layout, range of services)?
b Would you say that Whalton was a rural or urban settlement? Give reasons for your choice.

Fig. 5.2 (right) Settlement types and patterns.

5.2 Rural and urban settlements

We divide settlements into two basic types – rural and urban (Fig.5.2). Unfortunately, it is not always easy to distinguish rural from urban settlements. This is partly because there is no one definition of an urban (or rural) place agreed by everyone. For example, some countries measure the population size; some use the proportion of the population working in non-rural activities; and some the density of buildings. Some even use all three measures!

However, we can be sure that those settlements whose inhabitants are mainly involved in agriculture are rural. We recognise three types of rural settlement: isolated farms, hamlets and villages.

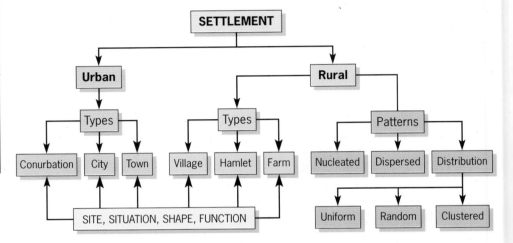

5.3 Rural settlement patterns

The distribution of farms, hamlets and villages in an area is called the **rural settlement pattern**. Here we look at two aspects of rural settlement patterns: nucleation and dispersion, and distribution.

Fig.5.3 (below) A nucleated village.

Nucleation and dispersion

The basic unit of all rural settlement patterns is the farm. A farm is an agricultural workshop and tied to the land it uses. In some areas farms cluster together to form villages and hamlets. This is a **nucleated** settlement pattern (Fig.5.3, Fig.5.4). Such patterns are widespread in lowland Britain, where, in the Middle Ages, peasants farmed the land co-operatively. Nucleation also occurs where water is only available in a few places – for example at springs or wells. Because water is so vital, settlements group together at these **wet-point** sites. Good examples of settlements at wet-point sites are the spring-line villages of Abbotsbury and Portesham at the foot of the chalk escarpment in South Dorset (Fig.5.6 and Fig.5.10).

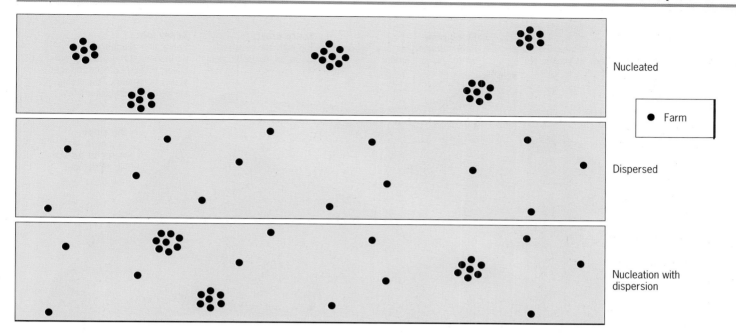

	Nucleated
● Farm	
	Dispersed
	Nucleation with dispersion

In highland Britain isolated farms are the most common settlement pattern. **Dispersed** settlement patterns are typical of regions where the agricultural land is poor (Fig. 5.5). Here each farm needs a large area of land to be self sufficient. As a result, individual farms are widely scattered and population densities are low. But nucleated and dispersed patterns are the extremes. In reality, most settlement patterns are a mixture of isolated farms, hamlets, and villages (Fig. 5.4).

Fig. 5.4 (above) Nucleated and dispersed settlement patterns.

Fig. 5.5 (below) Dispersed settlement in Upper Teesdale.

Table 5.1 Causes of nucleation and dispersion

Land quality	In highland Britain, a cold damp climate and poor soils mean that each farm needs a large area to produce enough food. This gives a dispersed pattern.
Social traditions	A long tradition of individual land ownership, as in Cumbria, leads to a dispersed pattern. Communal land ownership in lowland Britain in the Middle Ages produced villages and nucleated settlement patterns. In the eighteenth century, enclosure of medieval open fields in lowland Britain led to the dispersal of farms from villages into the surrounding fields.
Localised resources	Small 'islands' of dry land in marshy areas (e.g. The Fens or the Somerset Levels) leads to the clustering of farms. Springs and wells in chalk areas, where there are few surface streams, also cause nucleation.

The distribution of settlements across a region may be uniform, random or clustered. A uniform settlement pattern is where settlements are fairly evenly spaced. Usually, this is because there is an even spread of resources for farming (or in some cases, mining). Thus a plain where water and fertile soils are available everywhere is likely to develop a uniform settlement pattern. However, such patterns are unusual. In most regions resources are very unevenly distributed, so that settlements are absent in some areas, and concentrated in others. We refer to these patterns as either random or clustered.

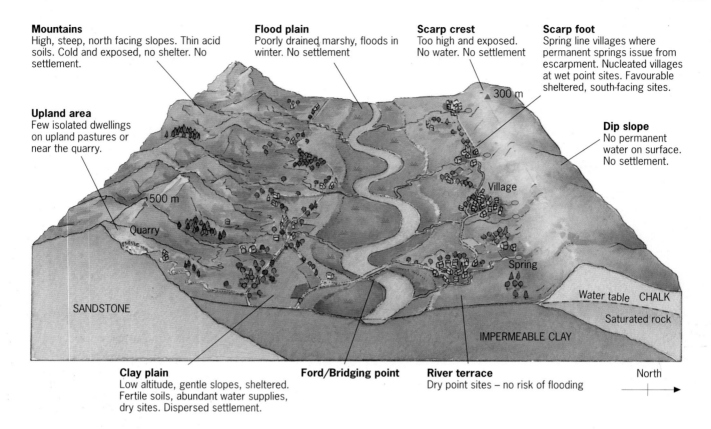

Mountains
High, steep, north facing slopes. Thin acid soils. Cold and exposed, no shelter. No settlement.

Upland area
Few isolated dwellings on upland pastures or near the quarry.

Flood plain
Poorly drained marshy, floods in winter. No settlement

Scarp crest
Too high and exposed. No water. No settlement

Scarp foot
Spring line villages where permanent springs issue from escarpment. Nucleated villages at wet point sites. Favourable sheltered, south-facing sites.

Dip slope
No permanent water on surface. No settlement.

▲ 300 m

Village

500 m

Quarry

Spring

SANDSTONE

Water table CHALK

Saturated rock

IMPERMEABLE CLAY

Clay plain
Low altitude, gentle slopes, sheltered. Fertile soils, abundant water supplies, dry sites. Dispersed settlement.

Ford/Bridging point

River terrace
Dry point sites – no risk of flooding

North

Fig. 5.6 Factors influencing the sites and distribution of settlement.

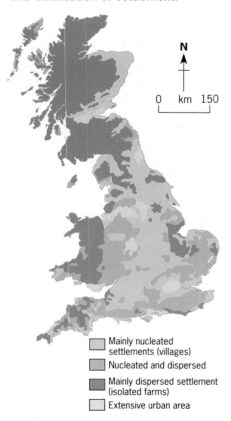

N

0   km   150

Mainly nucleated settlements (villages)

Nucleated and dispersed

Mainly dispersed settlement (isolated farms)

Extensive urban area

5.4 Rural settlement patterns in Britain

We saw in Chapter 2 that the Tees-Exe line divides Britain into two contrasting regions of geology and relief: the Highland Zone to the north and west, and the Lowland Zone to the south and east. Because physical geography has a strong influence on settlements, rural settlement patterns in north and west Britain are very different to those in the south and east (Fig.5.7).

In the Highland Zone rural settlement is sparse and widely scattered. Isolated farms and small hamlets are more common than villages (Fig.5.5). The reasons for this are both physical and economic. Poor soils and a cool damp climate have led to extensive livestock farming in the uplands (see Chapter 8). Because of the limited resources a large area of land is needed to support each family. As a result the settlement pattern is a dispersed one consisting of isolated farms. Also in the uplands there is a long tradition of independence. Farmers owned their own livestock and land, and so there was less need to co-operate and live in villages.

In the lowlands, where there is a warmer, drier climate and more fertile soils, cultivation is usually more important than livestock farming. This, has meant that farming is more intensive (Chapter 8). Land can be cultivated successfully even if farms are

Fig. 5.7 (left) Settlement patterns in Britain.

Fig 5.9 (opposite) Sketch map of the Wooler area.

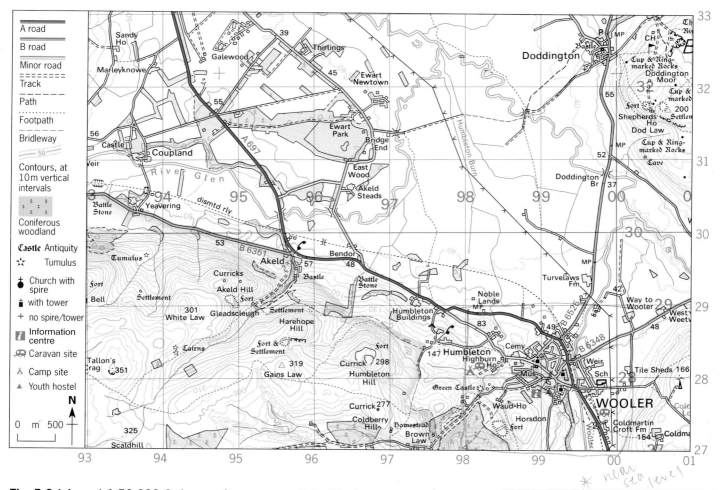

Fig. 5.8 (above) 1:50 000 Ordnance Survey map of the Wooler area.

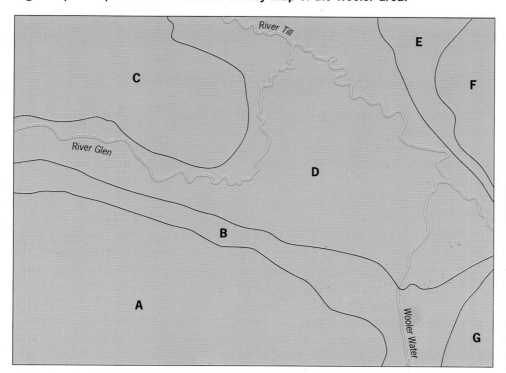

EXERCISES

4 Study Figure 5.8.

a What evidence is there that this area has been settled for hundreds of years?

b Name and give grid references for one of each of the following types of settlement: isolated farm, hamlet, village, market town.

c Copy Figure 5.9. Shade the areas A to G according to their density of settlement.Use the following divisions: fairly densely settled; sparsely settled; little or no settlement.

d Using evidence from Figure 5.8 give two possible reasons for the absence of settlement in
• areas A, F and G,
• area D.
• the concentration of settlement in B, C and E.

5 Settlement patterns

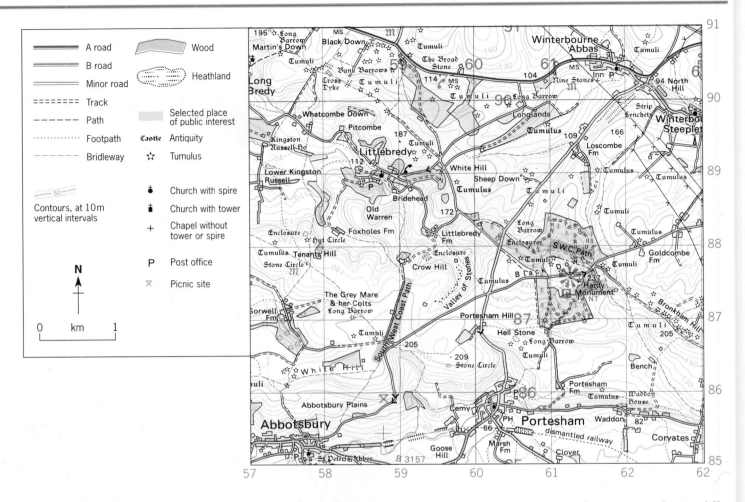

Fig. 5.10 1:50 000 Ordnance Survey map of the Abbotsbury area.

EXERCISES

5 Study Figure 5.10.
a What evidence is there that this area has been settled for hundreds of years?
b Draw a sketch (similar to Fig.5.8) of the area covered by Figure 5.10. Mark on it the main areas of settlement.
c* Explain for the area covered by the map extract:
• the distribution and density of settlement;
• the strongly nucleated pattern of settlement.
d* What other factors (not evident in Figs.5.9 and 5.10) might explain differences in the settlement patterns of Northumberland and Dorset?

clustered in villages. Social factors have also played a part. In the Middle Ages, under the feudal system, peasant farmers did not own their own land, but shared the cultivation of large open fields. This led to a nucleated settlement pattern.

5.5 Location, form and function

We have been studying groups of settlements which at a regional scale form settlement patterns. In this section we turn our attention to a smaller scale and investigate individual settlements. In particular we shall look at the characteristics of their site, situation, form (shape) and function.

Site

Site is the land on which a settlement is built (Fig.5.12). The original choice of location for a settlement was usually determined by the characteristics of the land on which it was built. Most settlements were established by groups of self-sufficient farmers, so that the site had to meet all the basic needs of the community. It had to provide land which was well drained, and not at risk from flooding; shelter from storms; a permanent water supply; and arable land for cultivation. A community would need pasture for livestock, and timber for building and fuel.

Fig. 5.11 Warkworth, Northumberland, from the air.

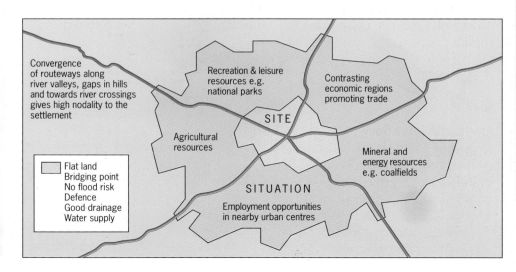

Convergence of routeways along river valleys, gaps in hills and towards river crossings gives high nodality to the settlement

Recreation & leisure resources e.g. national parks

Contrasting economic regions promoting trade

SITE

Agricultural resources

Flat land
Bridging point
No flood risk
Defence
Good drainage
Water supply

Mineral and energy resources e.g. coalfields

SITUATION

Employment opportunities in nearby urban centres

Fig. 5.12 (left) The site and situation of settlements.

EXERCISES

6 Study Figure 5.11.
a Draw a labelled sketch map to show the main features of Warkworth's site.
b Where was the main defensive weakness in the site of Warkworth? How was this strengthened in the Middle Ages?

7* Using Figure 5.8 describe the advantages of Wooler's site.

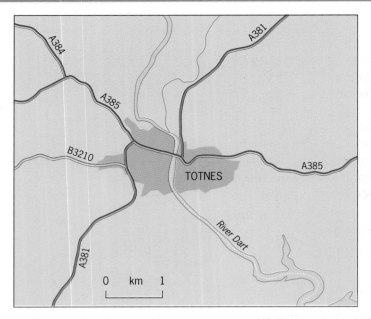

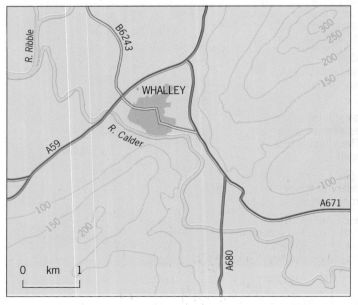

In the British Isles most settlements are at least a thousand years old. The fact that they have lasted for so long suggests that the sites were chosen by people who had a deep understanding of their physical environment.

The physical factors which influence site are the same as those affecting settlement patterns (Table 5.2). However, some sites were chosen not just because they provided shelter, fuel, food and water. These sites often had strategic importance. For example, some like Paris (Chapter 7) and London controlled river crossing points. Others had natural advantages, such as a commanding position, raised above the surrounding countryside, and the protection against attack given by steep slopes (e.g. Lincoln), river meanders (e.g. Durham) and the sea (e.g. Berwick-upon-Tweed).

Situation

Situation describes the location of a settlement in relation to the surrounding region (Fig.5.12). For example, a settlement situated between an upland region devoted to livestock farming, and a lowland region specialising in cereal crops might develop as a market centre. Trade between upland and lowland farmers could be conveniently carried out at a mid-point between the two contrasting regions.

Sometimes physical geography is responsible for a favourable situation. Examples include the lowest bridging point before a river widens out into its estuary (Fig.5.13); the convergence of several valleys; a gap in a range of hills, and so on (Fig.5.14). As a result of these physical advantages transport routes will focus on a settlement, increasing its accessibility (**nodality**) and often making it a hub for trade and industry.

Fig. 5.13 (top) Totnes, at the lowest bridging point on the River Dart.

Fig. 5.14 (below) Whalley, a gap town situated between the Ribble and Calder valleys.

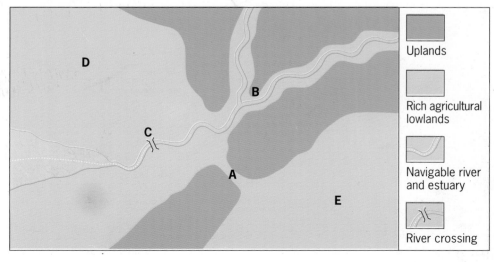

Fig. 5.15 (right) Favourable locations for settlements.

CASE STUDY

5.9 Service centres in Dorset

Dorset, in southern England, is a mainly rural county. The central and western areas of the county (Fig.5.21) have few manufacturing industries and most of the larger settlements such as Dorchester and Blandford Forum are market centres.

Table 5.6 Hierarchy of service centres

Order	Number of centres
1	14 (other service centres)
2	?
3	?
4	1 (Weymouth)

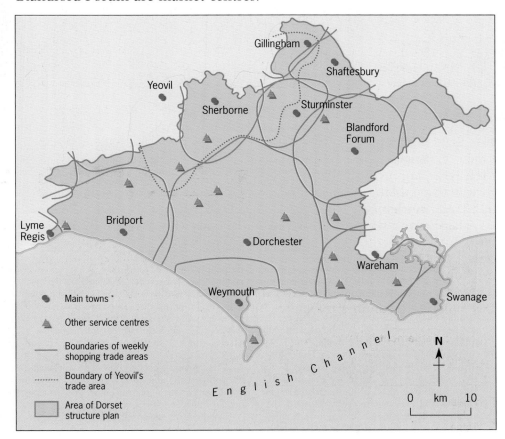

Fig. 5.21 (left) Distribution of service centres in Dorset.

Map legend:
- Main towns
- ▲ Other service centres
- Boundaries of weekly shopping trade areas
- ⋯⋯ Boundary of Yeovil's trade area
- ☐ Area of Dorset structure plan

EXERCISES

15 Study Fig.5.21 and Table 5.6.
a Which settlement in Figure 5.21 is likely to be the highest order service centre? Explain your choice. *Weymouth – highest trade area*
b Define your own hierarchy of service centres in Dorset by completing Table 5.6.
c How does the spacing of the main towns differ from the other service centres in Dorset (Fig.5.21)? Try to explain your answer.

EXERCISES

16a* Using the information in Table 5.7 draw a scattergraph by plotting the population (*y* axis) of each centre's trade area against retail floorspace (*x* axis). Draw in a best-fit trend line.
b* Describe and explain the relationship shown by your graph.
c* From the evidence of your graph, which centre's customers are most poorly served?
d* Figure 5.21 shows that Dorchester's trade area is more extensive than Weymouth's. Using the evidence of Table 5.7 can you suggest why this is unexpected? Try to suggest an explanation.

Table 5.7 Retail floorspace and population of trade areas in the main towns of Dorset.

Main towns	Retail floorspace (m²)	Trade area population
Blandford	8260	26164
Bridport	10860	24203
Dorchester	16720	36556
Gillingham	3810	8405
Lyme Regis	3620	3542
Shaftesbury	5290	10975
Sherborne	7430	16162
Sturminster	4180	12314
Swanage	4920	12009
Wareham	3250	19946
Weymouth	18580	70988

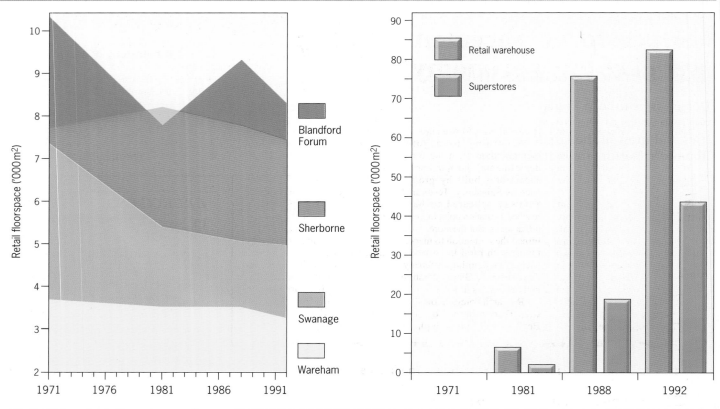

Fig.5.22 (top left) Changing retail floorspace for three Dorset towns.

Fig.5.23 (top right) Growth of super-stores and retail warehouses Dorset

Fig. 5.24 (above left) Dorchester's High Street.

Fig. 5.25 (above right) An article on the decline of Dorchester, Independent Magazine, 27.5.95.

One of the most beautiful and historic towns in southern England, Dorchester has very few modern buildings, and the traditional reluctance of the Duchy of Cornwall to allow its farming land to be converted to other uses has allowed it to remain as pretty and as artificially small as a bonsai tree. It is, in other words, the last place that you would expect to find superstores. But here they are: in Dorchetser, in the neighbouring town of Blandford Forum, and in other small and ancient market towns across Britain. And everywhere they spring up, they threaten to destroy the traditional town centre…

Superstores have spread from the cities where they first appeared nearly 30 years ago into every corner of Britain. But the difference now is not merely one of size. Once, a supermarket was opened in a town for the people of the town. But, as Britain has become a country of motorway bypasses, the retailing concept has changed: now you put a superstore by a bypass in order to draw the people who live alongside it. What matters is no longer ancient, rooted community but the new, mobile one; not the urban fabric but the road network. Looming at the edge of town, beyond cemetery and recreation ground, the superstore menaces the retailing heart of a town because it asserts a new principle of urban organisation where the car is king. In Dorchester, Tesco's crowded, glittering car park shows that the people are voting with their wheels. The FOR SALE and TO LET signs festooning the empty properties in the old centre send the same message…

Dorchester is one of the most beautiful towns in England. The Walks form the most elegant self-definition a town could possess, a perfect promenade. But, taking the spring air one evening, I passed not a single person on its entire circuit. A handful of shops in the town pique the curiosity; for the rest, from Dorothy Perkins to Kwik-Save, it's exactly what you'd expect. What soul the town has left is being eroded away.

5.10 From market town to ghost town

The shopping centres of many British market towns have declined steadily in the last 25 years (Fig 5.25). We can see such a decline in Dorset: market centres such as Blandford Forum, Wareham and Sherborne have all lost retail floorspace since 1971 (Fig.5.22). The main reason for this trend is the growth of large food superstores and retail warehouses on edge-of-town sites around major centres such as Weymouth, Poole and Yeovil (Fig.5.23).

Superstores 'threaten market town economy'

DAVID NICHOLSON-LORD
Consumer Affairs Correspondent

THE FUTURE of small market towns is threatened by out-of-town superstores and shopping centres, according to research by the Department of the Environment.

The three government departments with responsibility for retailing – Environment, Transport and Trade and Industry – yesterday conceded that despite a recent switch in government thinking aimed at helping the town centres retain their shops and supermarkets, powerful new trends were still pushing shops to the edge-of-town and out-of-town sites...

According to a joint memorandum from the three departments, the number of superstores built by groups such as Sainsbury, Tesco and Safeway appeared to have reached saturation point in many urban areas. But the stores have turned their attention to market towns with rural hinterlands, such as Godalming in Surrey, Cirencester in Gloucestershire and Sevenoaks in Kent.

Research commissioned by the Department of the Environment said such places risked losing the town-centre supermarkets which anchored their economy because of out-of-town competition.

It concluded: 'If competition eventually led to closure of the 'anchor' supermarkets, the result might be a decline of traditional town centres, with their variety of smaller retailers, and a loss of accessible facilities for those without a car.'

Since the mid-1970s, there has been a 27 per cent increase in the number of shopping trips, but a 90 per cent increase in the number of shopping trips involving a journey of more than 10 miles.

Apart from the effect on town-centre economies, this has resulted in a large rise in car-based emissions of carbon dioxide – the gas mainly responsible for global warming.

Fig. 5.26 An article on the impact of superstores, The Independent, 21.4.94.

EXERCISES

17 Read Figures 5.25 and 5.26. Then imagine yourself as either a parent with young children, an average income and a car, or as a pensioner on a low income without a car. Write a letter to your local newspaper giving (and explaining) your views about the relocation of supermarkets from your town centre to edge-of-town sites.

EXERCISES

18 a Describe the distribution of RDAs in England (Fig.5.27). **b** How do you think that the location of these areas might have contributed to their economic problems?

While many market towns have experienced declining trade, it is the smallest service centres in the remoter rural areas, which have been hardest hit. Today almost two in every five villages in England and Wales have no permanent shop; half have no primary school; and nearly three-quarters have no daily bus service.

There are several reasons for this. In some instances population decline has meant there are too few people to support local services. Employment in agriculture has fallen continuously in the last 30 years, and between 1993 and 2000 another 100,000 jobs are likely to disappear. Ageing populations in rural areas mean fewer children, and little demand for village schools. Meanwhile lack of public transport and poor roads often make commuting from remote areas difficult, and at the same time discourage businesses from locating there. And finally, rising car ownership allows people to travel to larger centres which offer more choice.

In Dorset, these problems have led to much of the county being classed by the government as a Rural Development Area (RDA) (Fig.5.27). RDAs receive government grants aimed at creating jobs (in tourism and small businesses) and keeping the villages alive.

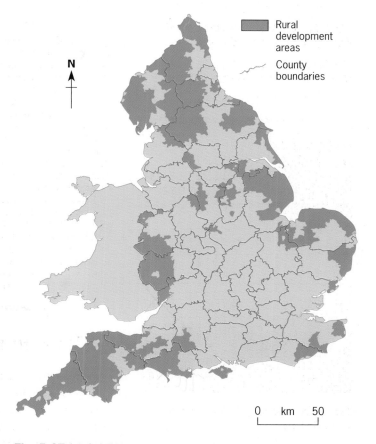

Rural development areas

County boundaries

N

0 km 50

Fig. 5.27 (right) Rural Development Areas in England.

5.11 Summary: Settlement patterns

Key ideas	Generalisations and detail
Settlements can be divided into rural and urban types.	• We recognise farms, hamlets and villages as rural: towns and cities as urban. However, there is no clear division between rural and urban types. Population size, employment in non-rural activities, population density and function are all used to distinguish urban from rural settlements.
Rural settlement patterns may be nucleated or dispersed.	• Nucleated patterns are dominated by villages. They are often associated with localised resources e.g. water, and a communal system of agriculture e.g. open field agriculture in medieval Europe. • Dispersed patterns consist of scattered isolated farms and hamlets. They are associated with pastoral farming, poor resources for farming, and a tradition of individuality. • In Britain nucleated patterns are more common in the Lowland Zone; dispersed patterns are typical of the Highland Zone.
Rural settlement may have uniform, random or clustered distributions.	• Clustered distributions are most common. They result primarily from the influence of physical factors such as relief, climate, soils, water supply etc. These factors can either attract or repel settlement. • Uniform distributions often indicate an even spread of resources e.g. on a lowland plain.
The characteristics of site, situation, shape and function are important features of individual settlements.	• Site refers to the land on which a settlement is built. In the past sites were chosen to provide resources (e.g. water, soil etc.) which would satisfy the basic needs of farming communities. • Situation is the location of a settlement in relation to the surrounding region. • Settlement shape is influenced by both physical factors (e.g. relief, drainage) and human factors (e.g. roads, planning). • Settlements have a variety of functions which increase with settlement size. The most important functions are residential, industrial and commercial.
Large settlements are central places or service centres.	• Settlements form hierarchies based on their importance as central places. Large settlements have many functions and serve large trade areas. They support high order functions (comparison goods/services, theatres, hospitals etc.) which require high threshold populations and have a large range.
Central place hierarchies in rural areas are undergoing rapid change.	• Car ownership (giving greater mobility) and new retail formats (e.g. edge-of-town super-stores) are responsible for the decline of retailing in many market towns. Smaller places, such as villages, are losing shops (also schools, GPs etc.) to larger centres. • There is a general decline of services in rural areas in the British Isles. Mobile services in rural areas are one response to this problem.

Fig. 5.28 A mobile veterinary surgery. Mobile services are a response to the decline of traditional services in rural areas.

6 Urbanisation and urban structure

6.1 Introduction

People first began living in urban settlements around 5500 years ago. These early towns and cities emerged in the fertile river valleys of the Tigris and Euphrates in modern Iraq, and the Nile in Egypt. This was no coincidence. A productive local agriculture was essential to create the food surpluses needed to support urban life. In these early examples agriculture was based on irrigation of the fertile valley soils (Fig. 6.1).

Towns and cities appeared much later in Britain. The first recognisable towns were built by the Romans, yet by AD 140 the total urban area in Britain was little more than 10 km². Compare this with 1995, when towns and cities covered nearly 28 000 km², or 11 per cent of the land area of the UK!

As towns and cities expand an increasing proportion of the population live in urban areas. We call this process **urbanisation.** Urbanisation has increased dramatically in the last 200 years. In 1800 only one in ten people in the world were city dwellers, but by 2000 the proportion will be almost one in two (Fig.6.3).

Globally, the effect of urbanisation has been very uneven (Fig. 6.4). The most highly urbanised countries are in the economically developed world. In the UK over 90 per cent of the population live in towns and cities. In the poorest countries, the proportion of city dwellers is often less than 30 per cent, although it is rising rapidly. Even so, two out of every three urban dwellers live in the economically developing world today (Fig. 6.2).

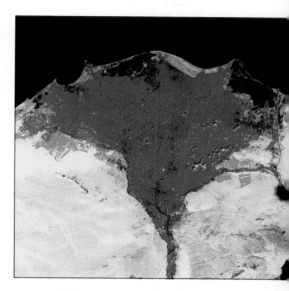

Fig. 6.1 Satellite image of the Nile delta. Irrigated land shown in red.

EXERCISES

Study Figure 6.2.
1a Where do most urban dwellers live today?
b In 1992 the world's population was estimated to be 5500 million. Calculate the percentage which was urban.
c Describe the distribution of urban and rural dwellers in economically developed and economically developing countries.(Fig.6.4).

Fig. 6.2 (below left) Urban and rural populations in the economically developed and economically developing countries,1992.

Fig. 6.3 (below right) The world's urban population,(in millions), 1950-2000.

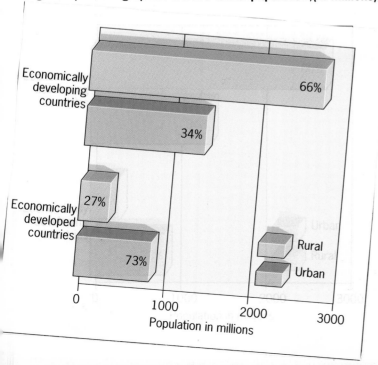

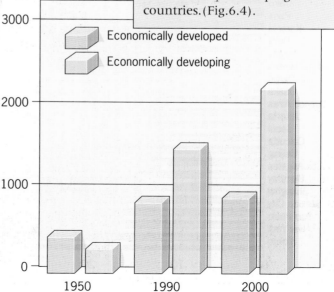

89

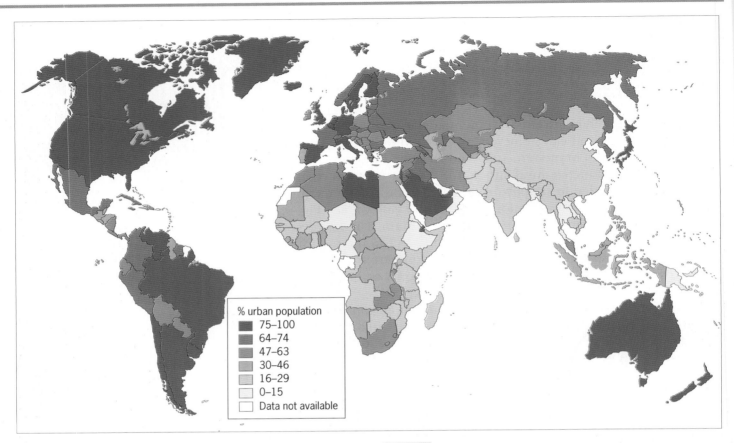

Fig. 6.4 (above) Distribution of the world's urban population.

Fig. 6.5 (below) Growth of the largest cities, 1994-2015

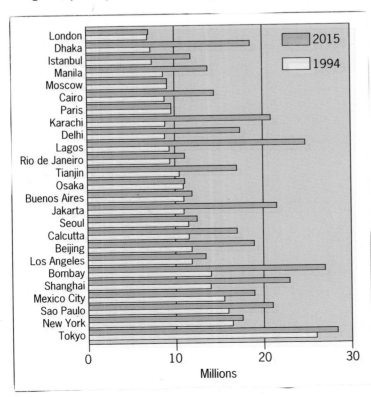

6.2 Urbanisation today

Urbanisation today is largely confined to the economically developing world. In the rich countries of Europe and North America rapid urbanisation took place in the nineteenth century linked with industrial development. However, by the mid-twentieth century it had almost come to an end.

One of the most striking features of contemporary urban growth is the increase in the number of large cities with a million or more people (Fig. 6.6). However, these million cities are overshadowed by the mega cities, such as Tokyo, Mexico City and Shanghai which contain huge populations, often over 10 million. (Fig. 6.5).

In 1950 there were 70 cities with more than one million inhabitants, mostly in the economically developed world. By 1982 the number had grown to 154, and by the end of the century there will be around 270. Most of these million cities are in the economically developing world. Many in Africa and Latin America began as administrative centres and ports in former colonies. They served as gateway cities, exporting minerals and agricultural products to the 'mother country' and importing

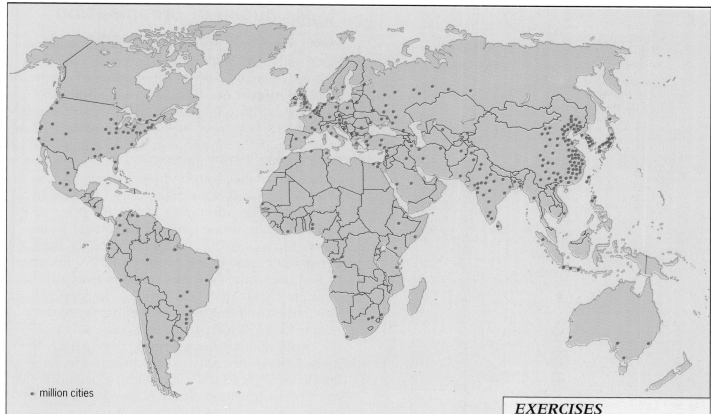

million cities

Fig 6.6 The million cities.

manufactured goods. These cities were the means by which the colonial power controlled the colony and exploited its resources.

Once the colonies had gained independence these large cities became the obvious place for overseas investment. Large trans-national corporations (TNCs) and foreign banks were attracted to these cities, which compared to the rest of the country often had well educated workforces, good roads, water supply, electricity and so on. Moreover, some of these cities are so large and wealthy that they are important markets for manufactured goods. Investment has created jobs which in turn have encouraged in-migration and rapid population growth. Sometimes, these cities have been so successful that they have grown to be several times bigger than their nearest rival. We have a special name for these cities: they are called **primate** cities.

Table 6.1 The primate cities of South America

% total pop in largest city		% total pop in largest city	
Argentina	35.5	Guyana	26.4
Bolivia	14.3	Paraguay	22.7
Brazil	12.5	Peru	30.7
Chile	37.3	Surinam	26.1
Colombia	15.4	Uruguay	41.6
Ecuador	16.5	Venezuela	14.1
French Guiana	67.3		

EXERCISES

2 Study Figure 6.6.
a How many million cities are there in: Europe, North America, Latin America, Africa, Asia and Oceania?
b Draw a pie chart to show the distribution of million cities by continent.
c What proportion of these cities are in the economically developing world?

3 Study Figure 6.5.
a Which was the largest city in the world in 1994?
b Which city will be the largest in 2015?
c Which city is likely to have the largest population increase between 1994 and 2015?
d* Plot the distribution of the world's 25 largest cities (in 1994) on a world map. Comment on their distribution.
e* Compare the growth of mega cities in the developed and developing worlds between 1994 and 2015.

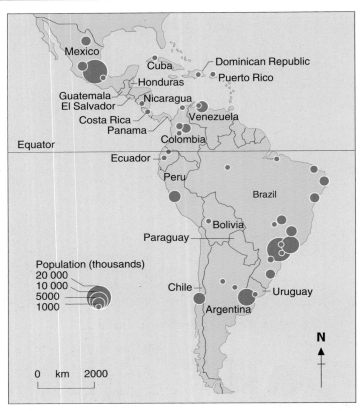

Fig. 6.7 Latin America's largest cities, 1990.

6.3 Causes of urbanisation

The population of a town or city can grow in two ways. Either through natural increase, where the number of births exceeds the number of deaths, or through **migration**. (People moving from one place to another.) In practice, urban growth usually combines both processes. About one third of the urban population increase in Africa and Asia comes from migration. In Latin America the proportion is somewhat higher – around 60 per cent.

Why do people move in such large numbers from the countryside into towns and cities? If we take Latin America as being typical then there is one simple answer: living conditions in urban areas are better than those in the countryside. For instance, in Peru the United Nations classifies nearly three-quarters of rural dwellers as being desperately poor, compared to less than one quarter of the people living in towns and cities (Fig. 6.9).

Among other things, rural poverty leads to higher infant mortality in the countryside. Poor families cannot feed their children a balanced diet, causing malnutrition. There is also a lack of safe water, fewer medical facilities, and poorer housing, all of which lead to higher infant deaths. Poverty creates the conditions for **rural-urban migration** (the movement of people from the countryside to the towns) However natural disasters and political unrest also play a part. In Latin America, drought (in areas like North-east Brazil) and floods and hurricanes along the Caribbean coast, have contributed to this movement. Guerilla and drug wars have given added impetus to population movements in several Latin American countries.

EXERCISES

4a Which countries in Table 6.1 are likely to have primate cities? Use an atlas to find the names of these primate cities.
b Study Figure 6.7
• Refer to an atlas and name the cities with more than 5 million people.
• Describe the distribution of the cities in Figure 6.7.
c What proportion are located on the coast?

CASE STUDY

6.4 Rural poverty in Ceara

Ceara state in North-east Brazil has a population of 6.5 million. It is one of the poorest regions in the country (Fig.6.8). Nearly one third of the population live in the state capital, Fortaleza, and another third in the countryside. The region is hot, dry and poor. Although poverty is common in the cities the poor are concentrated more in rural than in urban areas.

Malnutrition, especially among children, is high in rural areas. In spite of recent improvements, infant mortality rates are nearly three times higher than those in Sao Paulo, Brazil's largest city. Levels of education and literacy are low in the North-east region and are more like those in Africa south of the

Sahara than the rest of Brazil. Within the region illiteracy is much higher in rural than in urban areas (Fig. 6.10). Lack of education, particularly among young women, contributes indirectly to high infant mortality. Often children die from malnutrition and diarrhoea because their mothers lack knowledge of simple child care. Also simple cures such as sachets of rehydration mixture are not readily available.

Agriculture is the main employment in the countryside, and compared to industry its productivity and wages are low. Cotton is a staple crop, but was badly affected by pests in the 1980s and a severe drought in 1993. Irrigation is limited because there are few permanent rivers. One-sixth of Ceara's farmers are squatters with no legal title to the land they cultivate. Land ownership is very unequal. On the one hand hundreds of huge estates; on the other thousands of landless peasants. The state government has made attempts to redistribute land but so far land reform has made little progress.

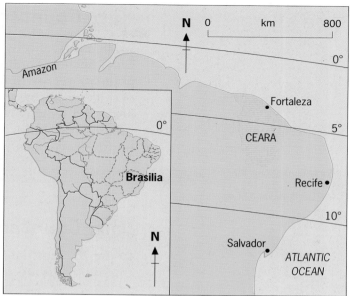

6.8

Fig. 6.8 (above) Ceara state in north-east Brazil.

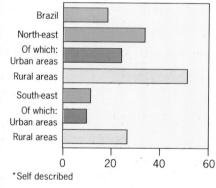

% of population aged 15 and over who can't read and write a simple note*

*Self described

Fig. 6.10 Levels of literacy in Brazil.

Fig. 6.9 Peasant house, Brazil.

Given conditions in the countryside, it is hardly surprising that Fortaleza attracts large numbers of migrants. Free sites with roads, water and power laid on, have been made available for migrants to build their own houses. Industry is growing, with investment from large firms from the south. There are plans for an oil refinery and a new deep water harbour for the port. Tourism is being developed – beachside hotels, and tall apartment blocks are springing-up everywhere in the city. Yet there is also acute poverty in the overcrowded slums (favelas) of Fortaleza. Here, a quarter of all families have no father and one man in three has no regular employment.

EXERCISES

5 We can divide the reasons for rural-urban migration into push and pull factors. Push factors are the negative reasons such as poverty which cause people to leave rural areas. Pull factors are the things which attract people to urban areas such as jobs and educational opportunities. Read through the case study of Ceara state. Make a list of push and pull factors which might cause rural-urban migration.

6.5 Counter-urbanisation

In the economically developed world, urbanisation has largely ceased. Cities such as London, Paris and New York are unlikely to show much population growth in the future (Fig. 6.5). In richer countries the balance of migration is now out of the city. Moreover, those who move out are the better off, leaving behind mainly the poor, unemployed and unskilled. This urban-rural shift is known as counter-urbanisation. It is common throughout the developed world.

CASE STUDY

6.6 Counter-urbanisation in the UK

In the UK most large urban areas have experienced an absolute decline in their populations since 1971. This decline was most rapid between 1971 and 1981, but it continued throughout the 1980s (Fig. 6.11). The areas losing population are the largest conurbations and cities. For example, between 1981 and 1991 Liverpool's population declined by 13.5 per cent; Birmingham's by 7.3 per cent; and Glasgow's by 15.5 per cent. In contrast there was rapid population growth in many of the rural counties of southern England: Buckinghamshire grew by 10 per cent; Cambridgeshire by 10.1 per cent; Norfolk by 6.3 per cent, and so on. Even some remote rural counties had a population revival. Thus Powys in central Wales grew by 6.1 per cent and Skye in North-west Scotland by 14.9 per cent.

The reasons for counter-urbanisation are complex. However, the essential causes are growing mobility, wealth, and the technological revolution, which have enabled the better off to leave the city for small towns, commuter villages and rural areas (Table 6.2).

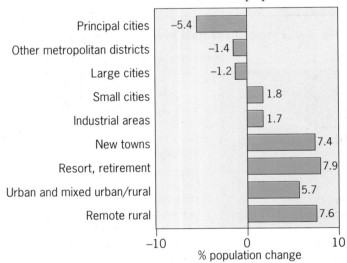

Fig. 6.11 Population change in Britain, 1981-1991.

Principal cities −5.4
Other metropolitan districts −1.4
Large cities −1.2
Small cities 1.8
Industrial areas 1.7
New towns 7.4
Resort, retirement 7.9
Urban and mixed urban/rural 5.7
Remote rural 7.6

−10   0   10
% population change

Table 6.2 Causes of counter-urbanisation in the UK

Retirement	Retired people, with generous occupation pensions, move to the environmentally attractive areas. This accounts for some of the rapid growth in coastal counties in southern England, such as Cornwall, Devon and Dorset.
Commuting	Higher income workers move out from the city to nearby smaller towns and dormitory villages where the quality of life (environment, education, crime) is seen to be better. Car ownership and motorways allow long distance commuting. Thus rural counties close to major cities and conurbations (e.g. Berkshire, Cheshire, North Yorkshire) have grown rapidly. Others move even further away and rely on fast train services (e.g. commuting from Lincolnshire to London).
Decentralisation of employment	Many offices have moved out of large towns and cities. Thanks to modern telecommunications (computers, faxes etc.) they can choose market towns, seaside resorts etc. Some employees can work from home using computer technology. There has been a similar rural movement by some industries, and the workforce has followed. Many high-tech firms have preferred locations in rural counties with good access to scenic areas like the Lake District, Scottish Highlands and Norfolk Broads.

6.7 Inside the city

When we look inside cities our first impression is frequently one of disorder. The layout of buildings, the network of streets and types of land use often seem quite haphazard. However, on closer inspection order does appear. For example, all cities have a clearly defined core – the **central business district** – dominated by shops and offices(Fig. 6.13). Some areas are devoted exclusively to manufacturing industry. Others are residential, with distinctive housing types reflecting the wealth and social standing of their inhabitants. But do these areas have a spatial pattern? Geographers think that they have and they have developed a number of simple models to describe the spatial pattern of cities (Fig. 6.12). However, no one city will exactly fit any model.

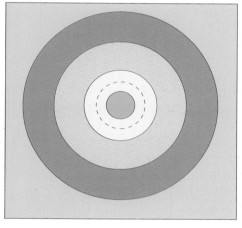

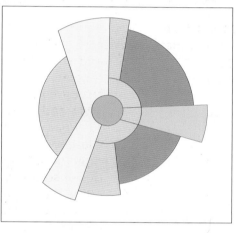

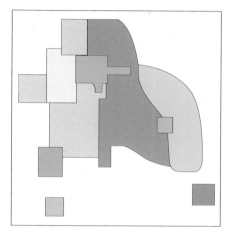

■ Central business district
□ Factory zone
- – Zone of transition
■ Zone of working men's homes
■ Residential zone
■ Commuter's zone

■ Central business district
□ Wholesale light manufacturing
■ Low class residential
■ Medium class residential
■ High class residential

■ Central business district
□ Wholesale light manufacturing
■ Low class residential
■ Medium class residential
■ High class residential
■ Heavy manufacturing
■ Outlying business district
■ Residential suburb
■ Industrial suburb

Zonal model
Land use is arranged in a series of concentric rings or zones around the city centre. The idea is that the city has grown outwards in all directions from its centre, adding new building around the edges. This process is rather like the annular growth rings of trees. It means that the urban fabric should get older towards the centre. The width of the zones varies according to the density of building

Sector model
Land use is arranged in wedges or sectors which radiate from the city centre. Growth follows a linear pattern along major transport routes or physical features such as river valleys. We assume that once a particular type of land use establishes itself in an area it attracts similar activities (e.g. industry) and repels dissimilar ones (e.g. high status housing).

Nuclei model
Distinctive land uses form small areas or nuclei such as the central business district, housing estates, industrial estates, office and retail parks etc. Often similar activities/types of land use benefit from being clustered together.

Fig. 6.12 Models of city structure.

6.8 How do cities grow?

Transport, more than any other factor, influences the size and shape of cities. Before 1850 urban transport was slow and inefficient. People were forced to live close to their work and to services. This resulted in a densely populated city with a circular form. In economically developed countries, city size and shape was transformed in the second half of the

Fig. 6.13 The central business district, Cardiff

nineteenth century. A series of transport improvements freed the better-off from living close to their work place. First there were horse-drawn trams and buses, then suburban railways and finally electric trams. Higher income groups moved out of the city and settled along the transport routes so that they could commute to work. The effect on the city was immediate. It grew outwards; great ribbons of housing following the lines of transport. In the late twentieth century this spreading process went even further. With the majority of households owning private cars, houses could be built anywhere provided that there were roads. So the areas between the ribbons were filled in and the city regained the circular form it had lost 150 years before.

6.9 Leicester

Leicester is a medium-sized British city in the East Midlands. Its origins go back at least to the first century AD, when the Romans established a settlement there. The settlement occupied a key site where the great Roman road called the Fosse Way (which ran from Exeter to Lincoln) crossed the River Soar. Roman Leicester was a walled settlement and prospered as a centre of administration and trade.

In the eleventh century the Normans built a castle on the Roman ruins and by 1086 Leicester had an estimated population of 2000. During the Middle Ages the town grew steadily as a market centre serving the surrounding agricultural region. Early industrialisation in the eighteenth century, based on hosiery and knitting, gave an impetus to growth. However, it was the building of the Grand Union canal and railways in the first half of the nineteenth century, that led to full-scale industrialisation. Large textile factories sprang up and replaced the old workshops. In the twentieth century many new industries were added – light engineering, shoe manufacture, machine tools, printing and electronics. Leicester also remained important as a market centre for surrounding rural areas as well as the administrative centre for Leicestershire and a major university town.

Land use patterns

Alongside population growth there was rapid expansion of Leicester's built-up area. The result was a series of distinctive land use **zones, sectors and nuclei** (Fig. 6.14).

Table 6.3 Population change in Leicester: 1801–1991

1801	17,000	1921	234,200
1851	60,600	1931	257,700
1871	95,100	1951	285,200
1881	122,400	1961	288,100
1891	142,100	1971*	284,200
1901*	211,600	1981	280,300
1911	227,200	1991	272,100

*major boundary changes

EXERCISES

6a Plot the growth of Leicester's population as a line graph.
b Suggest reasons for the rapid growth of Leicester's population in the nineteenth century.
c What evidence suggests that Leicester is currently affected by counter-urbanisation?

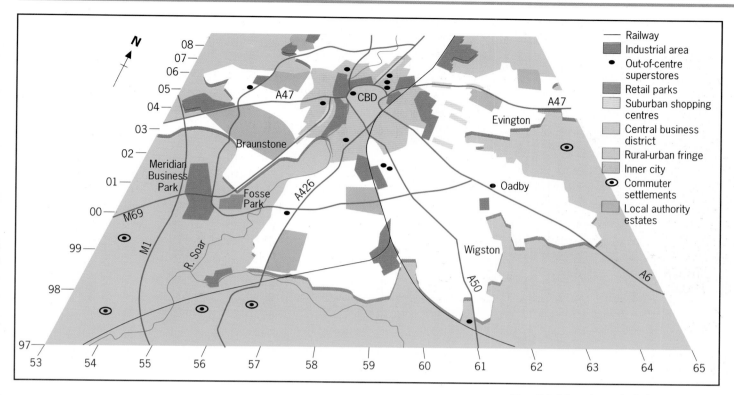

Fig. 6.14 Land use in Leicester.

Table 6.4 Land use patterns in a typical British city

CBD	The city centre is known as the central business district (CBD). It is a zone of shops, offices and entertainment. There are also important public buildings such as the town hall and cathedral. Land is scarce and in high demand. Thus multi-storey buildings dominate the centre (Fig. 6.13). Traffic and pedestrian flows are higher than in any other part of the city. Branches of national chain stores (e.g. Marks & Spencer, Boots) are found here. The advantage of a central location for shops is the access it gives to the largest number of shoppers. Roads and public transport converge on the centre giving unrivalled accessibility. With a large turnover these shops can afford the high rents for central sites and thus out-bid other potential land users.
Inner city	In most British industrial cities, rapid population growth between 1850 and 1914 added a distinctive zone to the urban fabric. This zone, consisting of high density housing, interspersed with factories and workshops is known today as the inner city. Before the development of efficient urban transport systems people needed to live close to their work. The original nineteenth century housing is terraced and is laid out in a simple grid pattern. Since 1960 the worst terraced housing has been replaced by modern terraces and high-rise flats, in a process called **urban renewal**.
Outer suburbs	Housing built since 1914 is generally of lower density and mainly consists of detached and semi-detached dwellings. These houses, either privately or council-owned are more spacious and have gardens. Often the built-up area is interrupted by open spaces such as parks and school playing fields.
	Many manufacturing, service and distribution firms have located in edge-of-town sites on industrial estates and business parks. The advantages of edge-of-town sites are: better access by goods vehicles along dual-carriageway ring roads and motorways; large, purpose-built single-storey factories with space for production lines and parking; cheaper land. Retailing has also moved out of the centre, with retail parks and superstores often lining major routeways.
Commuter zone	Many middle and high income families have moved out of cities into surrounding villages in the last 50 years. This is part of the counter-urbanisation process (section 6.2). Private car ownership gives people the mobility to commute from settlements which often lack any public transport services.

EXERCISES

7a With reference to Figure 6.12 construct a simple land use model for Leicester. Use three simple shapes: zones, sectors and areas.

b* Study Table 6.3 and Figure 6.14. Describe the differences between:
- the population growth in 1851–1911 and 1911–1991 in Leicester;
- the extent of Leicester's inner city and outer suburbs.

c* Account for the differences in timing between the most rapid growth of population and the most rapid growth of the built-up area in Leicester.

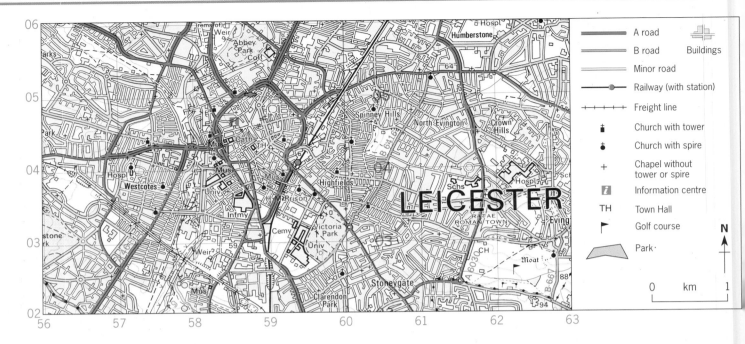

Fig. 6.15 Ordnance Survey 1:50 000 map of Leicester.

Population density

Population distribution is uneven in the city. In Leicester population densities vary from over 4000 per km^2 in parts of the inner city, to around 300 per km^2 in the outer suburbs. Few people live in the city centre. High rents in this area mean that housing cannot compete with shops and offices for space. The highest densities are found in the inner city, with its cramped terraced housing and high-rise flats. Remember that this is the oldest part of the city: most houses were built more than a century ago when living standards were much lower and people had to live close to their workplace. As we move to the outer suburbs densities drop steeply. There is more open space here; most houses are either detached or semi-detached and have large gardens.

Who lives where in the city?

Who lives where in the city depends on four factors: income; family status; ethnic group; and the distribution of housing types.

Better-off people have the widest choice. Usually they opt for larger houses, with the benefits of a pleasant environment and good access to schools, shops and other services. In contrast, poorer people may have little choice but to live in sub-standard housing, where overcrowding, poor services, pollution and crime are often serious problems.

Family status refers to the composition of households. For instance, whether a household consists of a single adult, a couple without children, a couple with young children and so on. This often influences where people live. Changes in family size are a common reason for people moving house. Usually this happens when a couple have children or when the children grow up and leave home.

Many western cities have large ethnic minority groups. Leicester is a good example: nearly one in three of the city's population belong to an ethnic minority group. Most of these people are of Indian origin.

They first settled in Leicester in the 1960s and 70s to work in the hosiery and knitting industries. This Asian population is highly concentrated in the inner city (Fig. 6.17) We call this **segregation** and it is typical of many ethnic minorities, in UK cities.

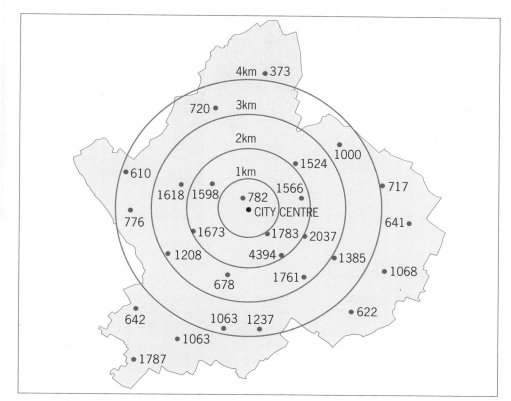

Fig. 6.16 Population density in Leicester, 1991.

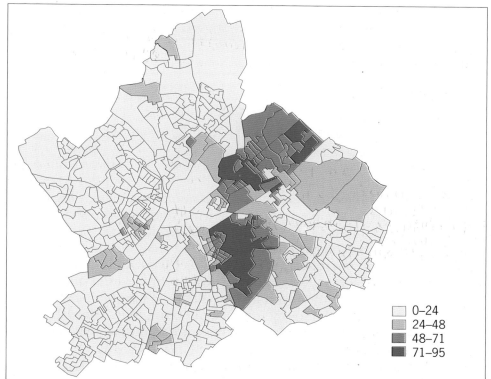

Fig. 6.17 Percentage of non-white population in Leicester.

EXERCISES

9a Using the information in Fig.6.16 calculate the average population in the five zones (1 – 5 km).

b Plot a line graph to show how the average density for each zone varies with distance from the city centre.

c Describe and explain the density trend shown on your graph.

d Draw three smaller graphs to show how the trend line might be modified as a result of the following: urban renewal (slum clearance) in the inner city; **gentrification** (middle income groups moving into refurbished terraced housing in the inner city); middle income groups moving into the commuter belt.

Fig. 6.18 (centre) Who lives where in the city?

Fig. 6.19 (top left) Council estate.

Fig. 6.20 (top centre) Inner city terrace.

Fig. 6.21 (centre right) Detached houses, leafy suburb.

Fig. 6.22 (bottom left) Gentrification – private riverside apartments.

Fig. 6.23 (bottom right) Retirement bungalow.

EXERCISES

10 Allocate the families in Table 6.5 to the houses in Figures 6.19 – 23. In each case explain your choice.

Table 6.5 Typical families in Leicester

	Family Income(pa)	Marital status	Age	Ethnicity	Family status
A	£50 000	married	45 & 44	white	2 children (12 & 10)
B	£12 000	married	30 & 30	white	3 children (7,5 &2)
C	£10 000	widow	75	white	children left home
D	£45 000	married	32 & 30	white	no children
E	£20 000	married	35 & 34	Asian	3 children (10,7 & 4)

We can explain ethnic segregation in a number of ways. First there are positive reasons: people want to live close to those who share their culture, customs and language, and use local services such as temples, mosques and ethnic food shops found in these areas. Second there are negative reasons, in particular the need to feel safe within a society which may often be hostile to minority groups. In Leicester and other cities with large Asian minorities, like Bradford and Wolverhampton, Asians are often attracted to the inner city because of its affordable terrace housing. As a rule they do not have a tradition of renting housing from the local authority.

6.10 Cities in the economically developing world

The simple models of city structure that we have looked at so far (Fig.6.12) describe urban land use patterns in the economically developed world. These models are not very helpful when we study cities in the economically developing world. Here history, traditions and economic conditions are very different, and there is a great variety of form. Indeed, the contrasts between cities in India and the Middle East, or Africa and South East Asia, are just as great as between those in the economically developed and economically developing worlds.

Latin American cities

Latin American cities are an example of one type of city in the economically developing world. From Mexico to Argentina they are quite distinctive. Most large Latin American cities were founded in the sixteenth and seventeenth centuries by the Spanish and Portuguese. They ran their Latin American empires from these cities. Often a colonial street plan survives in the city centre. Usually there is a central square around which are a church or cathedral, many administrative offices and the houses of the rich. Streets spread out from the square in a simple grid pattern.

Rapid urban growth during the twentieth century has led to a huge expansion of the built up area around this central core. In 1900 there were only three Latin American cities with more than one million inhabitants. Today, there are an estimated thirty-nine. This rapid growth has brought massive changes to city structure (Fig. 6.24). Although the central square and grid pattern of streets remains, a sector of commercial land use (shops, restaurants, entertainment etc.) now extends in one direction from the city centre. This is really an extension of the CBD. This sector is surrounded by the homes of the rich who use the services provided there. Beyond the CBD there are three residential zones. The housing gradually declines in quality and permanence towards the edge of the city – the outermost zone is one of squatter camps.

Bogota

Bogota is the capital of Colombia (Fig. 6.26). It lies at the foot of the eastern cordillera of the Andes at a height of 2600 metres. Like other large Latin American cities it has undergone rapid growth this century. Between 1938 and 1994 its population increased from 350 000 to

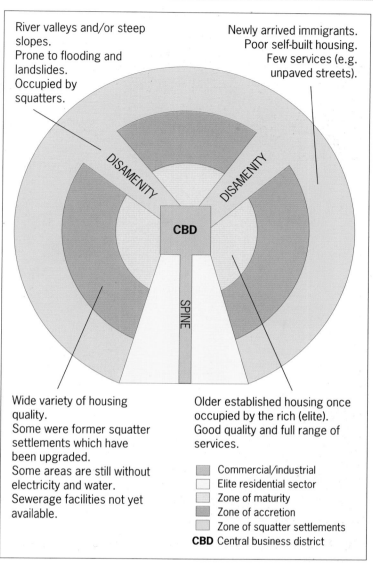

River valleys and/or steep slopes. Prone to flooding and landslides. Occupied by squatters.

Newly arrived immigrants. Poor self-built housing. Few services (e.g. unpaved streets).

DISAMENITY

DISAMENITY

CBD

SPINE

Wide variety of housing quality. Some were former squatter settlements which have been upgraded. Some areas are still without electricity and water. Sewerage facilities not yet available.

Older established housing once occupied by the rich (elite). Good quality and full range of services.

▨ Commercial/industrial
☐ Elite residential sector
▦ Zone of maturity
▩ Zone of accretion
▢ Zone of squatter settlements
CBD Central business district

Fig.6.24 (above) Model of the structure of a Latin American city.

Fig. 6.25 (below) Squatter family living beside the railway, Bogota.

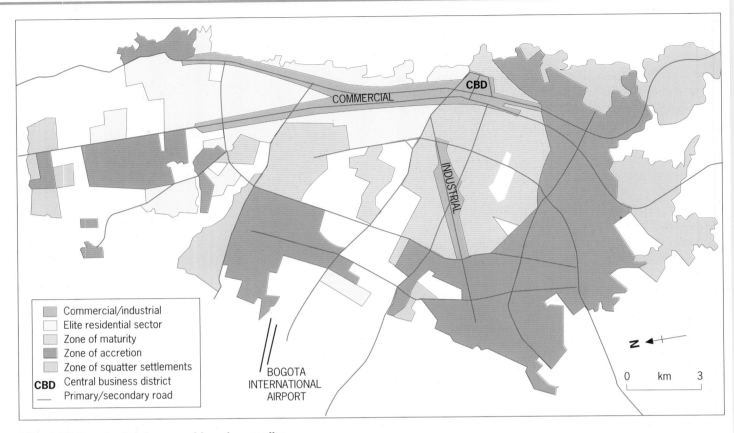

Commercial/industrial
Elite residential sector
Zone of maturity
Zone of accretion
Zone of squatter settlements
CBD Central business district
Primary/secondary road

COMMERCIAL
CBD
INDUSTRIAL
BOGOTA INTERNATIONAL AIRPORT

0 km 3

Fig. 6.26 Bogata: land use and housing quality.

EXERCISES

11 Study Figures 6.24 and 6.26.

a How does the actual lay-out of Bogota (Fig. 6.26) differ from the model's structure (Fig.6.24)? Suggest one possible reason for the differences.

b Describe, and suggest possible reasons for, the location of the elite residential areas and the zone of squatter settlements in Bogota.

c* Make a table and list the main differences in the distribution of high and low income groups in cities in the economically developed world and in Latin America.

5 400 000. A fifteen-fold growth in just over 50 years! Growth on this scale can only happen by migration. Migrants come to Bogota from all over the country.

Bogota is a city of contrasts. Its CBD is dominated by office blocks and skyscrapers. A four lane motorway leads into the centre and is lined with modern factories and the offices of major transnational corporations. This part of the city is like New York, Chicago and Los Angeles. The northern suburbs are modern. The residents are well-off and have American suburban lifestyles with access to modern shopping malls, McDonald's and Kentucky Fried Chicken restaurants. However, they are a tiny minority. Most people are poor and millions live in self-built housing without basic services, such as water, electricity and sewerage, around the edge of the city.

'The north of Bogota is typical of the way that Latin American cities have managed to create areas of 'modernity' amidst vast surrounding expanses of poverty. Should the visitor move further north or travel to the segregated south of the city a different world appears. The shops are smaller and offer a more limited range of goods. The housing gradually becomes more rudimentary, revealing the self-help nature of the building process. The plots are laid out in a regular pattern, but every house looks very different. Each family has built what it can afford. One plot has a well constructed two-storey home, the next a rickety shack.'

Alan Gilbert *The Latin American City*

6.11 Summary: Urbanisation and urban structure

Key ideas	Generalisations and detail
Cities first appeared around 5500 years ago	• The first cities were in the Middle East and Egypt. They were supported by food surpluses from irrigation agriculture in fertile river valleys
Urbanisation is an increase in the proportion of people living in towns and cities.	• Urbanisation has increased in the last 200 years. By AD 2000 half the world's population will live in urban areas. • Rapid urbanisation occurred in Europe and North America in the nineteenth century. • Today, urbanisation is concentrated in the economically developing world.
Today, urbanisation in the economically developing world is leading to the growth of mega cities.	• Mega cities have populations of 5 million and above. Many of these cities are primate cities and dominate industry, commerce and investment, in their respective countries.
Most urban dwellers live in the economically developing world	• Two out of three urban dwellers live in the economically developing world. Most of them are poor.
Urbanisation results from natural population increase and rural-urban migration.	• Rural-urban migration is the principal cause of urbanisation. People in the countryside in the economically developing world move to towns and cities because they think that living standards are better there.
Counter-urbanisation is an important trend in the economically developed world.	• In many economically developed countries the number of people living in conurbations and large cities is falling. Better-off people are moving out to the commuter belt and retiring to environmentally attractive areas. A few are moving to remoter rural areas.
Land use patterns in cities are known as urban structure.	• Most cities have a central business district surounded by distinctive zones, sectors and areas. There are clear differences in urban structure between cities in the economically developed and economically developing worlds.
In the economically developed world, population density generally declines with distance from the centre to the edge of the city.	• Few people live in the CBD. Densities usually peak in the inner city, and then fall steadily towards edge of the city. • Urban renewal and gentrification have led to an increase in the population of some central areas of cities.
Different social, economic and ethnic groups locate in different parts of the city.	• Different groups become segregated according to income and ethnicity. High income groups are able to choose areas with most advantages. Low income groups have little choice and often suffer many disadvantages. Ethnic minorities may cluster together out of choice.

Fig. 6.27 The central business district of Bogota.

7.1 Introduction

As cities grow, their demand for space and resources for housing, transport and jobs increases. Often these demands cannot be met immediately and a range of urban problems (Fig.7.1) such as homelessness, poverty, traffic congestion and air pollution develop.

In this chapter we shall investigate some of these problems and the attempts of planners to solve them. Most of the urban problems of the economically developed world are essentially the same as those of the economically developing world. However, their impact is often very different. Whereas in the cities of Europe and North America these problems may reduce the quality of life of urban dwellers, in the cities of Asia, Africa and Latin America they often concern the very survival of their inhabitants.

7.2 Poverty and urban decay

Poverty and urban decay are unevenly distributed within cities. In the UK, they are most often found in the inner city – the nineteenth-century zone of housing and industry which surrounds the CBD. Although nearly all inner city houses today have basic amenities, they are none the less cramped together, and there are few open spaces.

Fig. 7.1 Urban problems in the economically developed world.

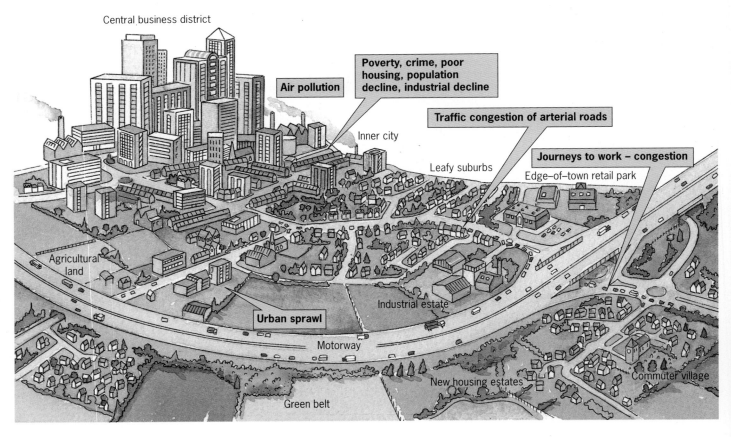

Central business district

Air pollution

Poverty, crime, poor housing, population decline, industrial decline

Traffic congestion of arterial roads

Inner city

Journeys to work – congestion

Leafy suburbs

Edge–of–town retail park

Agricultural land

Industrial estate

Urban sprawl

Motorway

New housing estates

Commuter village

Green belt

Table 7.1 Indicators of poverty in six Leicester wards

	% non-whites	% male unemployment	% families with no car	% council housing	% overcrowding
Belgrave	51.3	22.1	49.7	16.4	6.3
Latimer	70.8	23.9	0.6	21.0	7.5
North Braunstone	2.9	38.3	66.2	77.1	2.9
Saffron	5.3	30.8	51.3	52.2	5.3
Spinney Hill	82.5	31.7	52.6	8.3	12.0
Wycliffe	51.5	34.1	72.4	53.2	6.9
Leicester average	28.5	18.3	45.3	27.1	3.8

In Leicester, as in other UK cities, inner-city wards are among the poorest (Table 7.1 and Fig.7.2). Jobs are hard to find; overcrowding is common; levels of crime and drug abuse are high; and two out of three households cannot afford to run a car. In recent decades the better-off have moved to the outer suburbs, leaving behind an aged population, often on low incomes, and large ethnic minority groups.

However, it would be wrong to think that urban poverty is confined to the inner city. In many UK cities some of the poorest and most run-down areas are large council estates located on the edge-of-town. Although housing in these areas is newer and more spacious, unemployment, poverty and crime are high (Table 7.1). In some cases the problems have been made worse by local authorities deliberately choosing to house difficult families in the most run-down council estates.

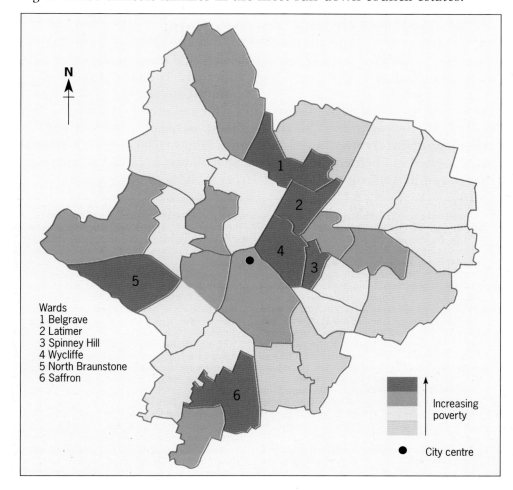

Wards
1 Belgrave
2 Latimer
3 Spinney Hill
4 Wycliffe
5 North Braunstone
6 Saffron

Increasing poverty

● City centre

Fig. 7.2 Distribution of poverty in Leicester, 1991.

Fig. 7.3 Multi-storey flats Nechells Green, Birmingham.

EXERCISES

2 Read Figure 7.4.
a What was 'system building' and why do you think it was favoured as a method of house building?
b In what ways were the high-rise flats an improvement on the slums?
c What disadvantages of living in the high-rise flats in Hyde Park and Hulme are mentioned?

Fig. 7.4 An article on high-rise flats the *Guardian*, 9.89.

7.3 Housing - the high-rise solution

In the 1960s and 1970s many British cities undertook huge **urban renewal** schemes. Vast areas of slum housing in the inner city were cleared and replaced by multi-storey tower blocks (Fig.7. 3). Although the new flats had amenities such as baths, showers and central heating, which the slums lacked, they soon proved unpopular with tenants. Re-housing broke up the tight-knit communities of the inner-city slums. Often the tower blocks were poorly built, expensive to heat and suffered from condensation and poor sound insulation. They were unsuitable both for families with young children and for old people. Vandalism and crime became increasingly difficult to control. So bad were the problems, that some local authorities decided it was cheaper to demolish their high-rise blocks and build conventional terrace and semi-detached housing instead. Thus massive tower blocks such as at Hulme in Manchester and Hyde Park in Sheffield (Fig.7.4), which were barely 25 years old, were demolished in the early 1990s.

The large-scale urban renewal of the 1960s and 1970s was very expensive. It was abandoned in the 1980s and replaced by a policy of up-grading older housing – urban renovation. Improvement grants were given to householders. This proved cheaper, more effective and more popular than complete urban renewal.

7.4 Dereliction and employment

Until the 1980s little attempt was made to tackle the problems of dereliction and unemployment in the inner city. The inner city lost many jobs between 1960 and 1980. As inner-city factories closed, new businesses preferred edge-of-town sites which offered better road access, more space for expansion and cheaper land. Between 1981 and 1984 the government created eleven Enterprise Zones (EZs) (Fig.7.5). Several were located in blighted inner cities. The idea was to attract new businesses and jobs to run-down areas. Firms locating in EZs enjoyed

High hopes

'YOU have only to look at a terrace of Georgian or Regency houses to see that uniformity of design and architectural merit can go together. What we have done before we can do again. We must afford to bring a new deal to those who still live in conditions of dreary squalor; and we can afford good design.'

Recent though it may sound, the message is 26 years old, and it was given by Geoffrey Rippon, extolling the virtues of system buildings – those very tower blocks and multi-storey estates now condemned for recreating the dreary squalor they were supposed to sweep away.

Few innovations have ever created such high hopes as system building, a method of construction using factory-built panels put together like giant Lego pieces. Homes came off the production line like cars.

Hyde Park, in Sheffield, and Hulme, in Manchester both include huge crescent shaped blocks cutting a swathe through the cities.

In Hulme, children still play among the overflowing rubbish bins. Metal coverings are bolted to the doors and windows of empty flats, yet vandals still force their way in. At least 12 000 people are still thought to live here, although the squatters make estimates difficult.

'When they were first built they were marvellous. People cramped and living with their parents at last had a home of their own. They came out of back-to-backs with tin baths and shared outside toilets into flats which had as much hot water as you wanted. You could have a bath every day,' said Mrs Blackband.

'The problem was that people came from different areas into these flats. It took a long time to build a community. Now that people have reached that stage, it's time to move on again.'

'These flats were not the right sort of place for families with children. A gust of wind would take a pushchair off the decks, ' said Mrs Bower. 'But the good things here should be remembered too. Old people don't die of hypothermia in council flats like these with their central heating systems.'

The grandeur of the 18th century inspired the council to call Hulme's crescents after Robert Adam and John Nash. But in Manchester the names have come to denote rats and roaches, concrete spattered with graffiti and heating systems that do not work.

These are big enough problems but the tenants have committed themselves to keeping the consultants to a much wider brief – to looking at problems such as a lack of jobs and poor health care.

Like Hyde Park, Hulme has been used as a dumping ground for people with nowhere else to go. Former mental patients have frequently been housed in the area. A survey of the estate by a voluntary drugs project collected 400 used syringes and needles from the streets.

a ten-year exemption from local taxes and were unhindered by planning controls.

In 1981 the government launched a second initiative to tackle the inner-city problem – urban development corporations (UDCs). They were responsible for much larger areas than EZs. Their main aim was to reclaim derelict land (Fig.7.6), build new roads and thus provide new sites which would attract businesses. The government provided some money, but the bulk of investment was to come from the private sector. There were thirteen UDCs in all (Fig.7.5). The first two were London Docklands and Merseyside Docklands. The London Docklands was the most successful UDC. (See Chapter 11). By 1990 it had almost completed the redevelopment of the Isle of Dogs and Surrey Docks including London's highest office tower at Canary Wharf (Fig.7.7). Docklands was linked to central London by a new light railway and an extension to the underground (Jubilee tube line). However, in the early 1990s, Docklands was hit by recession. The firm that built Canary Wharf went bankrupt and five years after completion Canary Wharf was only half occupied.

Enterprise Zones created few new jobs and were expensive. After 1984 no new ones were designated. Even so, two of the UK's most success-ful edge-of-town shopping centres were in EZs. Metro Centre at Gateshead was built on the site of a derelict power station, and Merry Hill at Dudley on the site of a former steel works. Major environ-mental improvements were achieved in UDCs in port areas like Merseyside and derelict industrial areas such as Sheffield's Don Valley. In London many offices moved from the City to Docklands but provided few jobs for local people. New housing was also largely for higher income groups, which caused resentment among local people.

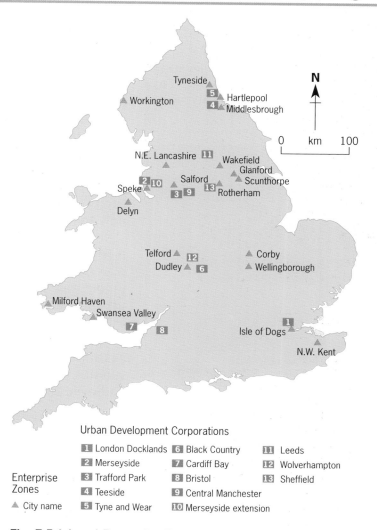

Urban Development Corporations

Enterprise Zones

▲ City name

1 London Docklands	6 Black Country	11 Leeds
2 Merseyside	7 Cardiff Bay	12 Wolverhampton
3 Trafford Park	8 Bristol	13 Sheffield
4 Teeside	9 Central Manchester	
5 Tyne and Wear	10 Merseyside extension	

Fig. 7.5 (above) Enterprise Zones and Urban Development Corporations in England and Wales.

Fig. 7.6 (below left) Derelict land in the Don Valley, Sheffield.

Fig. 7.7 (below right) Canary Wharf in London's Docklands.

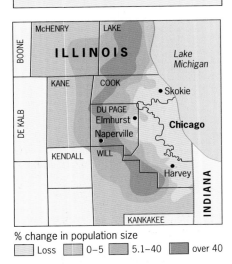

% change in population size

Loss | 0–5 | 5.1–40 | over 40

Fig. 7.8 (above) Population change in Chicago 1970-90.

Green belts
Major urban areas

Fig. 7.9 Green belts in Britain.

7.5 Urban sprawl

Every year 11 000 hectares of rural land in England are swallowed up by building. But the number of people living in towns and cities has hardly changed in the last twenty years. Why is this? There are several explanations. First, there are more households (e.g. young adults leave their parents earlier, couples split up, etc.). Second, more people can afford larger houses, which take up more space, and there has been a boom in second homes. And third, businesses have followed people to new sites in the suburbs. Here, on the edge of the city, farmland has been converted to shopping centres, office parks, industrial estates and new roads.

This loss of countryside to towns and cities is called **urban sprawl**. It has been recognised as a problem in Britain since the 1930s. In North America where there is more space, urban sprawl has been a less urgent problem. Even so, planners in the USA are beginning to accept that urban sprawl is wasteful and cannot go on forever. Chicago already sprawls across 9,800 km². Between 1970 and 1990, an area of farmland roughly equal in size to Berkshire was engulfed by the city. Meanwhile, as Chicago expanded into the countryside (Fig.7.8), sites in the inner suburbs were abandoned and left derelict. In 1994 the city of Chicago had over 2000 vacant manufacturing sites.

The fight against urban sprawl

In the UK, planners decided that **green belts** were the best way to stop urban sprawl. Green belts are areas of rural land around conurbations and large cities (Fig.7.9). Within these green areas strict planning controls operate to prevent urban growth. As well as stopping urban sprawl, green belts provide countryside for recreation and leisure for urban dwellers.

In the last 60 years green belts have been effective in slowing urban sprawl, but they have a number of disadvantages. Sometimes they protect poor soils and land of little scenic value from development while higher quality land beyond the green belt, which is not protected, becomes urbanised. Those who gain most from green belts tend to be the higher income groups who can afford to live on the edge of the city. Poorer people, living in the inner city and often without cars, may derive few benefits from green belts. But the biggest weakness of green belts is that they cannot stop a city from expanding. They simply interrupt its growth, which continues beyond the green belt.

Because of these disadvantages many European countries have used a different approach. For example, in Copenhagen in Denmark (Fig.7.11) planners have opted for **green wedges**. These wedges radiate from the city centre and are separated by corridors of growth. They give everyone equal access to green areas and at the same time allow for controlled expansion of the city.

7.6 Planning for urban growth: new towns

We have seen that green belts do not stop cities from growing.

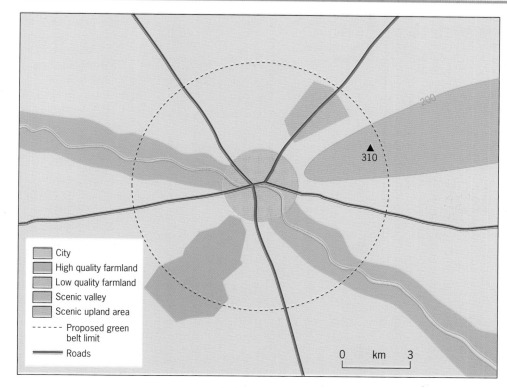

City

High quality farmland

Low quality farmland

Scenic valley

Scenic upland area

- - - - - Proposed green belt limit

Roads

0 km 3

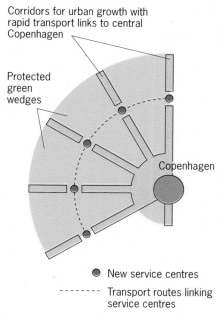

Corridors for urban growth with rapid transport links to central Copenhagen

Protected green wedges

Copenhagen

● New service centres

- - - - - - Transport routes linking service centres

Fig 7.10 (above left) Green belt or green wedge?

Fig. 7.11 (above) Green wedges plan for Copenhagen

Therefore, alongside green belts there needs to be provision for transferring the growth elsewhere. In the UK, overspill (surplus) population from large urban areas has been moved to purpose-built new towns sited beyond the green belt (Fig.7.12).

New towns in South-east England

Up until 1939, London's growing population was housed in estates on the edge of the city. This led to urban sprawl. By 1945 there was an acute housing problem in the capital. Many houses were slums and there were housing shortages caused by bombing and the lack of building during the war. Around one million people needed re-housing in 1945. A radical plan was proposed to solve the problem. A green belt, on average eight kilometres wide, was thrown around the capital. Meanwhile the overspill population was moved to eight new towns and to several expanded country towns outside the green belt (Fig. 7.13). The new towns were to be self-contained communities with their own employment, rather than commuter settlements for London. They had populations between 30 000 and 60 000 and were built from scratch on **greenfield sites** (farmland). Similar plans were adopted around most of the other conurbations in the UK.

By the mid-1960s the situation had changed. The population of the South-east of England had grown more rapidly than expected. It was forecast that population growth would continue into the 1980s, adding an extra three and a half million people. Thus, in 1964, a further three new towns were planned. They were located well outside London's commuter range and were bigger than the original eight new towns. Milton Keynes was built on a greenfield site, but Northampton and Peterborough were built onto existing centres.

EXERCISES

4 The city in Figure 7.10 is expanding. Planners provisionally decide to put a green belt around the city. Is this the best solution?

a Describe the disadvantages of the proposed green belt.

b* Copy Figure 7.10 and replace the green belt with five green wedges and five growth corridors.

c* Explain the advantages of your green wedge plan over the plan for a green belt.

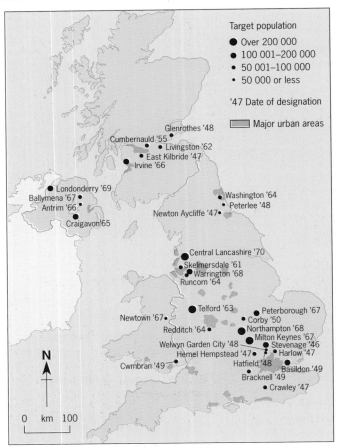

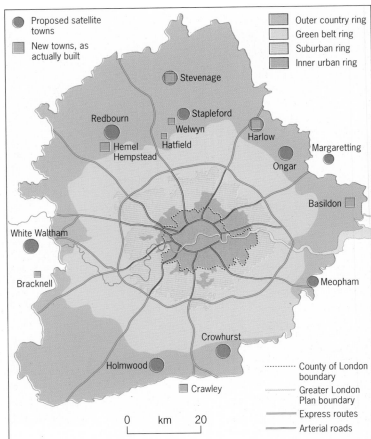

Fig. 7.12 (above) New towns in the United Kingdom.

Fig. 7.13 (above right) The plan for South-east England, 1945.

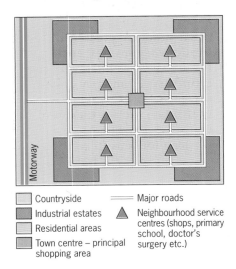

Fig. 7.14 (above) A typical new town plan.

Fig. 7.15 (right) The layout of Harlow new town.

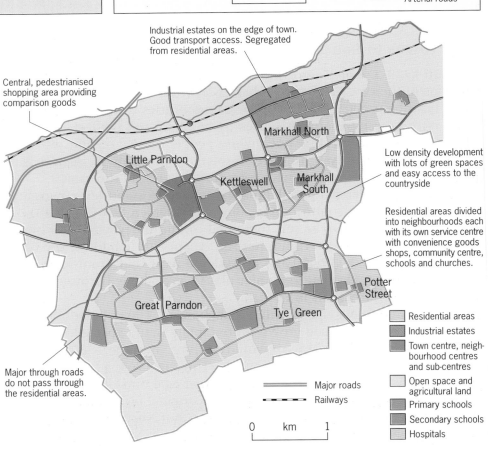

Fig. 7.16 Harlow from the air.

7.7 Traffic congestion

Traffic congestion is a major problem in most large cities. The average speed of traffic in central London today is only 15 kph: no more than it was 100 years ago. Why? The central areas of our cities – narrow streets with roads converging on the central business district – were not designed for the motor car. Also, since 1960, car ownership in the UK has increased rapidly. Today, three out of every five families own a car. The resulting traffic congestion wastes time, costs money and causes pollution.

Cities have responded to traffic congestion in a number of ways. They have built ring roads to divert traffic from the centre and express-ways to give easy access to the centre. They have encouraged motorists to leave their cars in the suburbs with park-and-ride schemes. They have restricted parking in city centres and devised elaborate one-way systems. Some cities have invested in new public transport systems such as Tyne and Wear's rapid transit railway (Metro), and the tramway systems of Sheffield (Supertram) and Manchester (Metrolink).

Tyne and Wear Metro

The Tyne and Wear Metro is an integrated rapid transit system serving the Tyneside conurbation. Developed in the 1980s from the region's underused rail network, its purpose was to relieve road traffic conges-tion. The hub of the system is a 6.4 kilometre underground railway in central Newcastle. Forty-five stations on the network link Metro

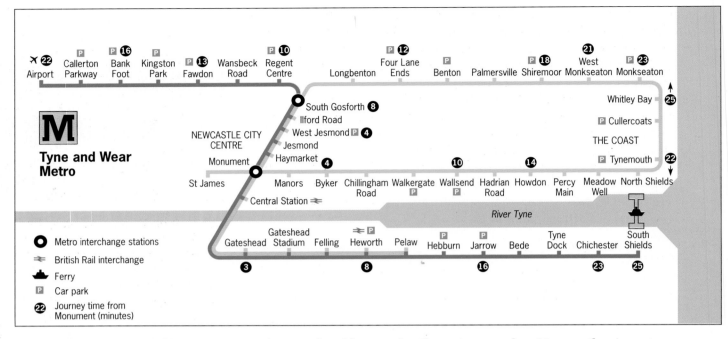

Fig. 7.17 Tyne and Wear Metro.

stations to local bus and rail services, and to Newcastle airport (Fig 7.17). Trains run every 10 minutes during the day, and every 5 minutes during the morning and evening rush hours. Parking is available at most stations, encouraging passengers to use the Metro as a park-and-ride scheme. The Metro has been a great success. It carries around 50 million passengers a year and there are plans to extend the network to Sunderland by 1997.

7.8 Air pollution in cities

Large concentrations of industry, housing and traffic in cities often leads to air pollution and health hazards. Winter smogs were commonplace in British cities until the mid-1950s. In London in December 1952, 4000 people died from breathing problems caused by the effects of smog. The smog was a lethal mixture of soot and sulphuric acid produced by coal-burning factories, power stations and domestic fires.

Thanks to laws which prevent coal burning in British cities, London's 'pea soupers' are a thing of the past. However, Beijing, the capital of China is not so fortunate. It still depends heavily on coal for power and suffers from smogs similar to those once found in London. So bad is the problem that 'oxygen bars' have been opened where people can sit and rent an oxygen mask to recover!

Although coal burning no longer causes smog in western cities air pollution has again become a serious problem. Nowadays, a murky brown photochemical smog caused by gases from car exhausts often covers our cities. On still sunny days these gases (nitrogen oxide and hydrocarbons) react with sunlight to produce ozone. Ozone is a poisonous gas and high concentrations are dangerous to asthma sufferers and people with breathing difficulties.

Los Angeles is particularly badly affected by photochemical smog (Fig.7.18). On most days a dirty haze hangs over the city making it the

EXERCISES

6 Study Figure 7.17. This is a **topological** map. It consists of a series of routes (lines between stations) and nodes (stations). Unlike other maps it does not show actual distances or the real position of places.
a Why do you think that the Tyne and Wear Metro uses a topological map rather than a conventional map?
b Which stations are • most accessible • least accessible? Explain your answers.
c What physical feature reduces the overall accessibility of the Metro?
d Suggest one additional route which would increase overall accessibility on the Metro.
e Where would you change trains if you travelled by the most direct route from
• South Shields to Palmersville
• Airport to Wallsend?

land around the city creating dust; exhaust fumes from three million road vehicles; heavy industries such as oil refining; and inadequate refuse and sewage disposal.

It is not just the air in cities in the developing world that is polluted. In Santiago, Chile, untreated sewage is pumped directly into the city's rivers and canal. Water from these sources is used for irrigation and pollutes crops. This probably causes the city's high rate of typhoid.

CASE STUDY

7.11 Nairobi

Nairobi is Kenya's capital and largest city. Like other large African cities its population growth in recent years has been rapid and unstoppable (Fig.7.29). By 1995 its population was 1.5 million – a fourfold increase in 30 years. At current growth rates its population will double by 2010. This growth is due both to rural-urban migration and natural increase.

Fifty-five per cent of Nairobi's population lives in shanty towns (Fig.7.30) on just 6 per cent of the city's residential land area. The supply of cheap housing in Nairobi has not matched its rapid growth of population. Overcrowding is a major problem. Dwellings usually consist of a single room. In an average household there may be four or five people and it is not uncommon for households to share accommodation. Thus the average density of population in Nairobi's shanty towns is around 73 000 per km² (Fig.7.32).

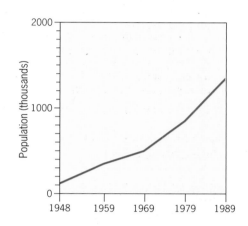

Fig. 7.29 Population growth in Nairobi 1948-89.

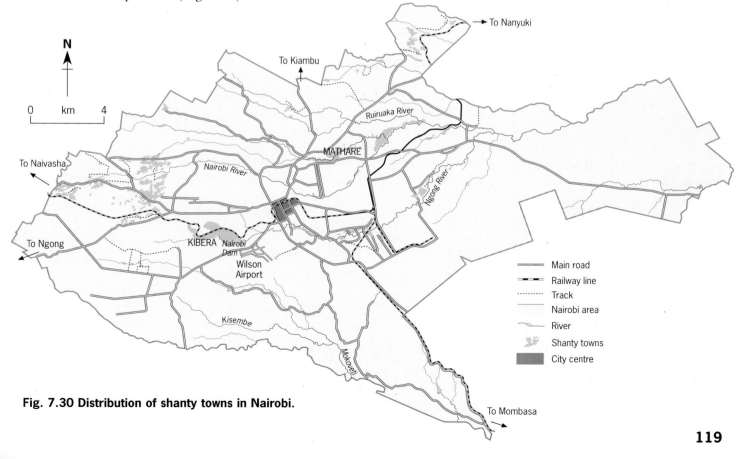

Fig. 7.30 Distribution of shanty towns in Nairobi.

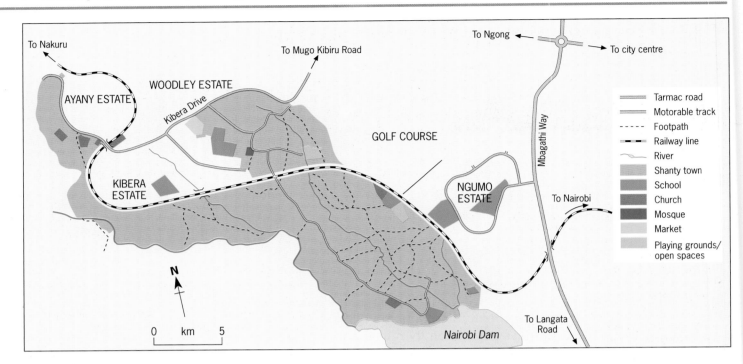

Fig. 7.31 Kibera shanty town, Nairobi.

EXERCISES

12a Study Figure 7.30 and describe the possible advantages and disadvantages of the location of shanty towns in the following areas: edge-of-town; around the city centre; close to rivers.
b Study Figure 7.31 and describe one possible advantage and one disadvantage of the site of Kibera.

Fig. 7.32 Mathare valley the largest slum in East Africa.

Kibera is Nairobi's largest shanty town (Fig 7.31). Situated seven kilometres from the city centre it has a population of nearly 250 000. Imagine a city the size of Leicester where the houses are made from mud, wattle and corrugated iron. There is no planning and the city authority provides neither roads, sewerage, drainage, water nor electricity. This is Kibera. Most people have to buy water from tanks (or kiosks) at inflated prices because there are not even standpipes. Some use the nearby Nairobi Dam, which is polluted. The only sanitation consists of pit latrines which may be shared between anything from 50 to 500 people. Human excreta litters the settlement and is a major health hazard, particularly in the rainy season when the area floods. There is no official refuse collection. Refuse is thrown anywhere and contributes to the health hazards. Mortality rates are high owing to overcrowding (the average population density exceeds 110 000 per km², poor sanitation, lack of clean water, poor drainage and accumulating refuse. Diarrhoea, associated with poor sanitation and poor water supplies, is a major cause of death in children. Few houses have electricity and there is no street lighting. Roads are unpaved.

There are 20 clinics set up by non-government and community organisations which are free, and just five primary schools. Average class sizes are 50-60 pupils. One-third of children receive no education beyond primary school. Around two in five people have paid employment as casual labourers, watchmen, servants, cleaners, etc, mainly in the nearby industrial areas and estates and in the city centre. Of the self-employed about one-third (mainly women) cultivate small plots of land, and the rest have small business interests. Trading of food, cigarettes, fuel, and water is most popular, but there is a wide range of more productive activities in Kibera, including metal working, machinery repair, carpentry, construction and shoe making.

7.12 | Summary: urban problems and planning

Key ideas	Generalisations and detail
Cities in both the developed and developing worlds face a number of urgent problems.	The main urban problems are: • housing (shortages and sub-standard housing) • poverty • congestion and environmental pollution • urban sprawl The scale and seriousness of these problems is greater in the economically developing world
Planners have tackled the inner city problems of poverty, crime, unemployment and urban decay in the economically developed world with a variety of measures.	Planning responses include: • Urban renewal involving demolition of slums and the building of high-rise flats e.g. Hulme in Manchester and Sarcelles in Paris • urban improvement • enterprise zones and urban development corporations.
Urbanisation and the increasing number of households in the economically developed world has led to urban sprawl.	• In the UK green belts have been used to curb urban sprawl. • Green wedges and corridors of growth have been preferred in some other European countries such as Denmark, France and the Netherlands,
New towns have been developed to accommodate rising urban populations and increasing numbers of households in the economically developed world.	• In the UK new towns have been developed around major conurbations and beyond the green belt. In South-east England a total of eleven towns have been built since 1945. • Paris has five new towns located in the city's twin axes of development.
Congestion in the central areas of cities in the economically developed world has led to the decentralisation of economic activities.	• New towns have assisted decentralisation. Shopping centres, industrial estates and office parks (e.g. La Défense in Paris) have been developed outside the CBD or at edge-of-town locations in the last 30 years.
Air pollution from traffic is a serious hazard in the urban environment in all large cities.	• 50 years ago air pollution was caused by burning coal leading to winter smog. This is still a problem in poorer countries such as China. • In the economically developed world air pollution is mainly caused by car exhausts. The result is photo-chemical smog and high concentrations of ozone. Restrictions on the use of private cars in cities and new public transport schemes (e.g. rapid transit, trams, etc.) aim to reduce both pollution and congestion.
Urban problems in the economically developing world concern the very survival of city dwellers.	• Rural-urban migration caused massive expansion of cities in the economically developing world since 1950. City authorities do not have the resources to solve housing, employment and environmental problems. Most people rely on self-help. This is evident in the growth of (a) huge shanty towns and (b) informal employment based on small-scale services and businesses. Environmental concern has little priority at the moment in most cities.

8 Agricultural systems

EXERCISES

1a Agriculture produces a wide range of products used in manufacturing industries, as well as food. List some of these products and say what they are used for.

b Using the information in Table 8.1 draw pie charts to show the distribution of the world's agricultural workforce and the value of agricultural output.

c What proportion of the world's agricultural workforce is in economically developed countries?

d What proportion of the world's agricultural output is produced by economically developing countries?

e* Suggest reasons why economically developed countries produce a large proportion of the world's agricultural output with only a small agricultural workforce.

8.1 Introduction

Agriculture is 'the control and use of plants and animals for the production of food, and fibre and raw materials for industry'. In a number of ways agriculture differs from other economic activities. Unlike manufacturing and services, agriculture relies heavily on the physical environment, and the life cycles of plants and animals. Both are largely outside the control of farmers. Agriculture also uses a larger proportion of the Earth's surface (around 37 per cent of the land area) and provides more employment worldwide than any other economic activity (Table 8.1).

Table 8.1 Agricultural workforce and the value of agricultural output (1990)

	% world's agricultural workforce	% world's agricultural output by value
Economically developing:		
Africa	12.5	5.5
Middle East	3.2	4.3
South and S E Asia	31.2	16.1
East Asia	44.0	12.5
Latin America	3.9	8.4
Economically developed:		
North America	0.32	11.4
Western Europe	1.2	19.4
Eastern Europe	2.9	11.8
Other	1.2	10.5

Fig.8.1 The farm system.

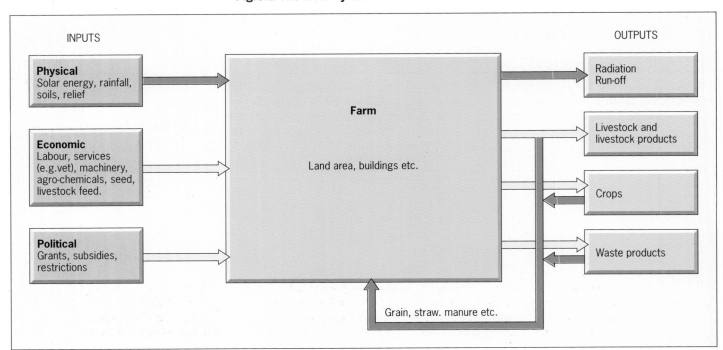

INPUTS

Physical
Solar energy, rainfall, soils, relief

Economic
Labour, services (e.g.vet), machinery, agro-chemicals, seed, livestock feed.

Political
Grants, subsidies, restrictions

Farm

Land area, buildings etc.

OUTPUTS

Radiation
Run-off

Livestock and livestock products

Crops

Waste products

Grain, straw. manure etc.

8.2 Agricultural systems

Farms are both ecological and economic systems(Fig. 8.1). First let's consider a farm as a simplified ecosystem (See 4.2). It contains only those species of plants and animals which are useful to the farmer. Useless species which compete with crops and farm animals (weeds and pests) are destroyed. Like any ecosystem, a farm relies on climatic inputs of solar energy and rainfall, and on plant nutrients from the soil. However, unlike natural ecosystems most farms are not self-sustaining. Crops and livestock products which leave the farm remove nutrients from the system which must be replaced by artificial fertiliser.

Table 8.2 How farmers can modify the physical environment

Physical environment	Modifications
Rainfall	Irrigation. By diverting rivers or using underground supplies farmers can supplement direct rainfall.
Temperature	Crops can be grown in glasshouses (heated or unheated) or under cloches. South-facing slopes can be cultivated.
Soil	Soils can be drained. If they are acidic they can be limed. Shortages of nitrogen, phosphorus, potassium etc. can be made up by using fertiliser. Field operations e.g. ploughing can alter the structure.
Relief	Steep slopes can be terraced.
Wind	Shelter belts, hedgerows and other wind breaks protect crops.
Pests and diseases	Crops can be sprayed with pesticides. Weeding.

Agriculture is also an economic system. For example, in addition to climatic and soil inputs, an arable farmer in the UK would also require inputs of labour, seeds, agro-chemicals (fertilisers, pesticides) and machinery. These are all part of the costs; and, as commercial farmers aim to make a profit, the value of farm outputs must exceed costs.

8.3 Types of agriculture

Usually we refer to types of agriculture in one of three ways: by the dominant **enterprise**; by the intensity of production; and by the extent to which farming is for cash.

The simplest definition is by enterprise – what a farm produces (Table 8.3). Thus we refer to dairy farms which specialise in milk production; arable farms where crops dominate; and mixed farms where there is a combination of both crops and livestock.

The intensity of production is more concerned with farming methods. Intensive farming involves high inputs of labour, agro-chemicals, machinery, etc. per hectare, with resulting high outputs or yields per hectare. Often this type of farming develops where land is either in short supply or has very high fertility. Typical intensive farming systems are wet rice cultivation in South-east Asia (Fig.8.5) and horticulture in Holland. Extensive farming is just the opposite. Low inputs per hectare give low outputs per hectare. Very large farms or those with poor quality land often use extensive methods, such as hill sheep farming in the Pennines and cattle ranching on the High Plains in the USA (Fig. 8.6).

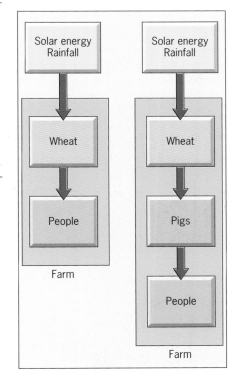

Fig. 8.2 Food chains in subsistence farm systems.

Table 8.3 Major world agricultural systems

Type	Features	Examples
SHIFTING CULTIVATION	Temporary cultivation of small plots cleared in the rainforest. Simple technology e.g. axes, hoes. Low population density. Plots abandoned after harvest	Tribal groups in rainforests of Amazonia, central and west Africa and south-east Asia.
NOMADIC PASTORALISM	Constant movement of pastoralists and livestock in search of pasture and water. A response to meagre environment resources. Cattle kept in wetter areas. Sheep, goats and camels in drier parts. Extensive use of land.	Semi-arid areas such as fringes of the Sahara and Arabian deserts. Also movements between upland and lowlands known as transhumance e.g. Zagros mountains in Iran.
PEASANT AGRICULTURE	Sedentary cultivation around permanent settlements. High population density. Farmers may be tenants, sharecroppers or owner occupiers. They may own their tools and other working capital. Often highly labour intensive e.g. wet rice cultivation.	Easily the most important type of farming in the economically developing world. Found throughout Asia, Africa and Latin America. May be dry farming (based on direct rainfall) or irrigation farming. Wet rice cultivation in south-east and south Asia supports hundreds of millions of people.
PLANTATION AGRICULTURE	Cultivation of cash crops e.g. palm oil, bananas, tea, rubber, etc. for export. Crops grown on estates. Owned by foreign transnational companies e.g. Unilever, but using local labour.	Most plantation agriculture is based on tropical and sub-tropical crops and is found in the economically developing world.
HORTICULTURE	Intensive (both capital and labour) cultivation of soft fruit, vegetables and salad crops. Cultivation of small plots, much of it in glasshouses.	Mainly found in the economically developed world, serving large urban markets. Horticulture in the economically developing world is small-scale and related to the growth of air transport and international tourism.
MECHANISED ARABLE FARMING	Large-scale cultivation of cereals, sugar beet, potatoes, etc. Capital intensive. High inputs per person of agro-chemicals.	Middle to high latitudes in North America (prairies), Europe and Australia.
DAIRY FARMING	Intensive livestock farming for milk. Needs good transport links between farms and markets.	Middle to high latitudes in the economically developed world. Often found in regions of higher rainfall and heavier soils.
INTENSIVE LIVESTOCK	Pigs, poultry, calves, etc. produced indoors in intensive off-land enterprises.	Mainly found in the economically developed world where there is a market for expensive eggs and meat products.
EXTENSIVE STOCK RAISING AND RANCHING	Sheep farming and cattle raising in uplands. Cattle ranching and sheep in semi-arid regions. Extensive farming on poor land with low outputs per hectare.	Hill sheep in upland areas in Europe such as Highlands of Scotland. Ranching in semi-arid regions like the High Plains, USA and Pampas in Argentina.
MEDITERRANEAN AGRICULTURE	Based on traditional drought-resistant crops such as olives and vines. Also wheat and sheep. With irrigation, citrus fruits and salad crops are important.	Found in regions which have a summer drought e.g. Mediterranean basin, California, South Africa, south and west Australia, central Chile.

Commercial agriculture   Non-commercial agriculture

Finally there is an important distinction between commercial and non-commercial farming (Table 8.3). In the economically developed world, virtually all farming is commercial. This means that farmers produce crops and livestock products for sale, in order to make a cash profit. In the economically developing world, non-commercial agriculture remains important. In this system, farmers and their families grow crops mainly for their own consumption. What's left may be sold or traded for other products in local markets (Fig. 8.3). We often call this type of self-sufficient farming **subsistence** agriculture.

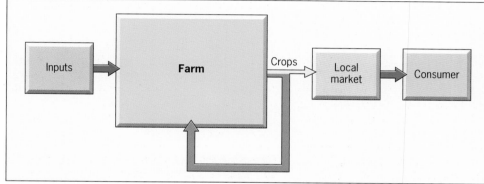

Fig. 8.3 (above) A non-commercial farming system.

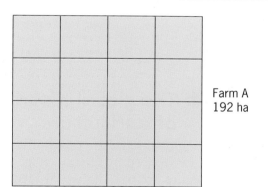

Farm A 192 ha   Farm B 12 ha

Fig. 8.4 (opposite) Farm size and farming intensity.

Fig. 8.5 (below left) Intensive rice cultivation in Bali, Indonesia.

Fig. 8.6 (below right) Cattle ranching on the High Plains, USA.

125

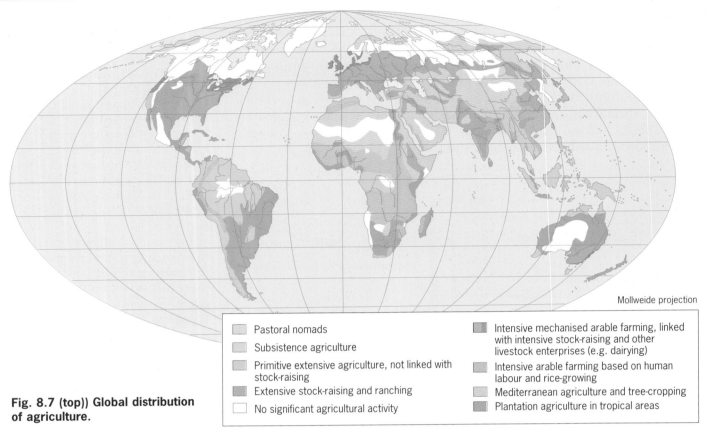

Pastoral nomads

Subsistence agriculture

Primitive extensive agriculture, not linked with stock-raising

Extensive stock-raising and ranching

No significant agricultural activity

Intensive mechanised arable farming, linked with intensive stock-raising and other livestock enterprises (e.g. dairying)

Intensive arable farming based on human labour and rice-growing

Mediterranean agriculture and tree-cropping

Plantation agriculture in tropical areas

Mollweide projection

Fig. 8.7 (top)) Global distribution of agriculture.

Fig. 8.8 (above) Arctic tundra, the Mackenzie Delta, Canada.

Fig. 8.9 (below) Hot desert, Wadi Rum, Jordan.

8.4 The global distribution of agriculture

At the global scale the distribution of agriculture is most influenced by climate (Fig. 8.7). Large parts of the planet are unsuitable for farming because they are either too cold or too dry. All crops have minimum requirements for heat. Growth usually begins when the mean daily air temperature rises above 6^0C. Moreover, temperatures need to be above this critical level for at least 120 days. As you go nearer to the poles, temperatures fall and the growing season shortens, until cultivation is impossible. This is the main reason why cultivation rarely extends beyond latitude 60^0 in the northern hemisphere.

Crops also have minimum moisture requirements. Thus the world's hot deserts, such as the Saharan, Arabian and Australian deserts, are simply too dry for cultivation unless water is available for irrigation. Extensive farming systems based on nomadic herding of camels, sheep, goats and cattle are found only around the edges of deserts. High mountains such as the Himalayas and Andes support few farming activities: as well as severe climates they also have steep slopes and thin soils.

8.5 Distribution of agriculture in the UK

At the national scale, climate is the most important factor affecting the distribution of agriculture. In the UK there is a simple pattern: the east is mainly arable, the west mainly pastoral (Fig. 8.10). Arable farming dominates the drier eastern side of the country. Here precipitation is between 600 and 800 mm which favours crops such as wheat, barley, oil seed, sugar beet and potatoes. Also the slightly warmer summers in eastern areas give crop production an added advantage.

In the west, precipitation is too high for most arable crops to be grown profitably, but is ideal for grass. Thus dairying and beef cattle are the leading enterprises in western areas. Pastoral farming is also found in the uplands. However, the harsh climate, steep slopes and poor soils limit farming to hill sheep and cattle rearing.

EXERCISES

5a Figures 8.8 and 8.9 show two harsh environments for agriculture. List the evidence in each photo which suggest that farming would be difficult in each environment.

b Suggest any actions that people could take to make farming possible in these environments (e.g. modifying physical factors Table 8.2; introducing special types of farming, etc.).

Fig. 8.10 (above left) Distribution of types of farming in England and Wales.

Fig. 8.11 (above right)The length of growing season in England and Wales.

Map legend (Fig. 8.10):
- Dairy cattle
- Lowland beef and sheep
- Upland beef and sheep
- Crops
- Mixed

Table 8.4

	July temp °C	Jan temp °C	Growing season (days)	Precipitation mm
Cheshire	16–17	4–5	250–275	?
Suffolk	?	3–4	225–250	?
South Devon	17–18	?	?	750–1500
Central Wales	16–17	3–4	?	?

EXERCISES

6 a Using the information in Figures 8.10, 8.11, 3.18, 3.19, 3.21, and 2.8, complete Table 8.4.

b Identify the main farming type in each region (Fig. 8.10).

c Explain how the physical factors in Table 8.4 might have influenced the choice of farming in each region.

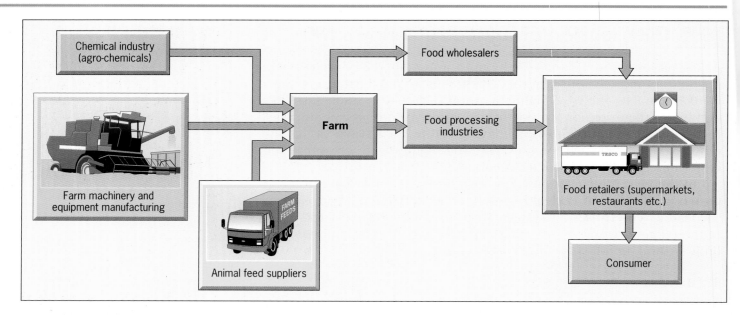

Fig. 8.12 The food system.

8.6 Agriculture and the food system

Farming is the production side of a chain of activities which eventually lead to food consumption (Fig. 8.12). This **food system** includes industries which supply essential farm inputs, such as agro-chemicals and machinery, and food wholesalers, food retailers and food manufacturers who handle the outputs from the farm.

Geographically, food systems vary in length. Some are worldwide; others extend no further than the farm gate. In economically developing countries, most farm produce is still consumed on the farm. This means that food systems are short. Those crops which are not consumed on the farm are probably sold in the local village market. In economically developed countries, food systems are much longer. For example, in the UK lamb is imported from New Zealand, citrus fruits from South Africa, coffee from Colombia and so on. However, even in the UK some food systems are short. Increasingly farmers (especially those living close to large towns and cities) sell directly to customers through their own farm shops and pick-your-own schemes.

Food retailers and the food system

Leading food retailers like Marks & Spencer (M & S), Sainsbury's and Tesco have an important influence on farmers, controlling what is grown, how it is grown and its quality. Although M & S gets most of its food from the UK it increasingly buys fresh fruit and vegetables from overseas. A new trend is that more and more of the UK's fresh food comes from economically developing countries. This means that geographically, food systems are becoming longer, and that farming, like manufacturing, is increasingly a global industry. Why is this?

One reason is that more and more customers want fresh foods all year round and not just for the few weeks when they are in season in the UK. Modern air freighting of highly perishable products such as strawberries and asparagus makes this possible. When M & S searches for new suppliers, climate is crucial. The most obvious sources are the tropics, where, providing water is available, farming is possible all year; or further south, where summer corresponds to the British winter.

M & S have recently established a successful trade in fresh runner beans with Zimbabwe. With its humid and tropical climate, Zimbabwe has the ideal conditions to supply the British market all the year round. Other advantages include: low labour costs (vegetables are hand picked) (Fig. 8.13); good air-freight links which mean that products can be on supermarket shelves within 24 hours of picking; facilities for grading, quality control, packing and bar coding. Exports from Zimbabwe's horticulture sector were worth nearly £40 million in 1995 and are growing rapidly. Apart from runner beans, other leading export crops are sweet corn, baby corn, peas, mange tout, plums, mangos and strawberries.

Fig. 8.13 Hand picking beans in Zimbabwe.

CASE STUDY

8.7 Shifting cultivation

Shifting cultivation is the traditional method of farming in the tropical rainforest (Fig.8.14). It is a form of subsistence agriculture, often combined with hunting, and practised by small tribal groups like the Iban in Sarawak in South-east Asia.

We saw in section 4.3 that the rainforest has very poor soils – so poor that permanent cultivation is impossible. Shifting cultivators get round this problem by making temporary clearings in the forest (about 2 ha for a family of six). The Iban make these clearings in June and July, and burn the leaves and branches in August which is a relatively dry month. The ash from the burnt vegetation fertilises the soil and allows cultivation for up to two years. Hill rice, which does not require irrigation, is the main crop. Seeds are sown directly into the ash using a simple digging stick.

Fig. 8.14 (above) Shifting cultivation in the Orinoco river basin, Venezuela.

Fig. 8.15 (left) Cycle of cultivation of the Iban.

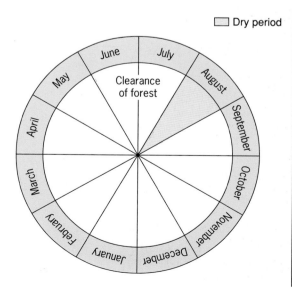

☐ Dry period

Timetable	
Date	
1.6	Begin clearance of forest plots.
1.8	Clearing complete.
14.8	Trees are burned.
18.9	Sowing of rice begins.
27.10	Sowing completed.
12.2	Quick ripening rice harvested.
26.3	Threshing of quick ripening rice.
22.4	Late ripening rice harvested.
2.5	Storing of rice.

NB weeding takes place from the completion of burning to the final harvesting of rice.

EXERCISES

9 Copy Figure 8.15 Add notes to your diagram about the sequence of tasks during the farming year using the timetable given in beside it.

Initially rice yields are good. However, cropping and heavy rainfall quickly removes plant nutrients from the soil, and weeds become an increasing problem. After two years, cultivation is no longer worthwhile, and the Iban abandon their plots and make fresh clearings in the forest.

Shifting cultivation is a **sustainable** type of farming. This means that it does no long-term damage to the environment, providing the intervals between cultivation are long enough to allow the forest trees to regenerate and the soil to recover its fertility. In the case of Sarawak a 15-year cycle of cultivation is needed. There are two threats to the sustainability of shifting cultivation. One is population growth which may force farmers to re-cultivate plots before they have recovered their fertility. The other is logging. In Chapter 4 we saw how commercial logging is devastating Sarawak's rainforests. If this continues for much longer then the shifting cultivators of this region will be forced to abandon their unique way of life.

CASE STUDY

8.8 Nomadic herding

Like shifting cultivation, nomadic herding is a response to harsh environmental conditions where resources for farming are too sparse to allow sustainable, settled agriculture. Although nomadic herding is found in some sub-Arctic areas and high mountain ranges, it is most closely associated with the fringes of tropical deserts like the Sahara (Fig.8.7).

On the southern edge of the Sahara Desert in Mauritania, rainfall averages only 100 to 250 mm. Because of this low and unreliable rainfall settled agriculture is impossible. Thus farmers have no option but to follow a nomadic existence. They keep cattle, camels, sheep and goats which, apart from longer stays at summer and winter encampments, are

Fig. 8.16 (left) Seasonal movements of nomads in Mauritania.

Fig. 8.17 (right) Mean annual rainfall in Mauritania.

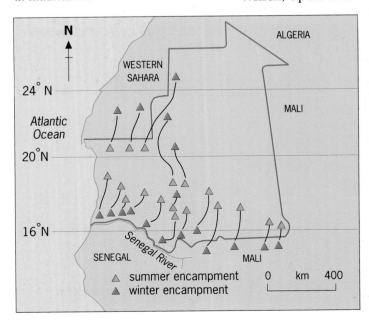

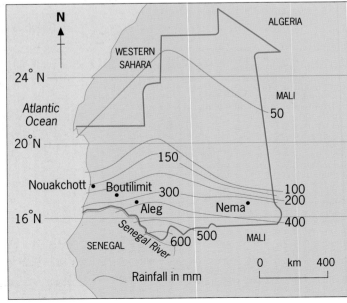

constantly on the move in search of water and pasture. They follow the seasonal rains, moving northwards between July and October, and spending winter in the south. Each year, and at the same time, they visit the same wells and pastures. A typical annual cycle might involve a journey of 800 kilometres (Fig. 8.16).

Nomadic herding is an extensive farming system. Meagre supplies of water and pasture mean that a large area is needed to support each animal. Thus output per hectare of meat, wool, milk, hides and other items is small. Food chains are short. Items that the nomads cannot produce themselves such as cereals, will be exchanged for livestock products with village cultivators.

Nomadic herding is a sustainable farming system, well adapted to a harsh environment. But like shifting cultivation it is currently under threat as a way of life. First, because governments wish to stop traditional migrations across international borders, and force the nomads to live in villages where they can be taxed; second, because population growth leads to more livestock and overgrazed pastures; and third, because of a long succession of drought years since the early 1970s. Drought greatly reduces the land's **carrying capacity** – its ability to support the nomads and their animals.

Southern Mauritania lies within the semi-arid ....belt. The rest of the country is desert, and apart from scattered ....is uninhabited. Nearly ....of Mauritania is too dry to support any kind of agriculture. The rains follow a predictable seasonal pattern. The winter is a period of .... Most rain falls between July and October, advancing from the south and gradually petering out northwards. The extreme south of Mauritania is the only part of the country which can support .... agriculture.

EXERCISES

10 Study Figures 8.16 and 8.17, then copy the paragraph opposite, inserting the missing words from the list below.

Missing words:
oases, drought, settled, Sahel, three-fifths.

CASE STUDY

8.9 Arable farming in eastern England

Grange Farm in North Lincolnshire is situated in the arable core of eastern England (Fig. 8.21). The local climate, relief and soils are ideal for most arable crops (Table 8.5).

The physical environment in this part of Lincolnshire places few limits on farming. Even so, the potato crop requires irrigation during most summers. Also Grange Farm lies very close to sea level. As a result the land has to be drained artificially. Pumps lift the water from the fields and into the nearby River Trent.

EXERCISES

11* Study Tables 8.5 and 8.6 and explain how physical conditions favour arable farming at Grange Farm.

Table 8.5 Grange Farm: physical geography

Altitude (m)	0
Mean July temperature (°C)	16.0
Mean annual precipitation (mm)	600 - 650
Growing season	March to November
Soils	Rich alluvial soils deposited by the River Trent.

Table 8.6 Crops yields: UK and Grange Farm

	Average yields per hectare	
	UK	Grange Farm
Wheat	6.5	10.0
Sugar beet	40.3	60.0
Potatoes	38.0	40.0

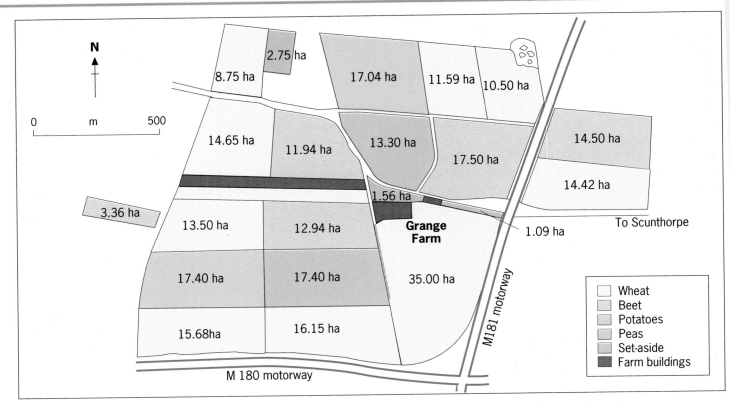

Fig. 8.18 (above) Lay-out and land use: Grange Farm.

Fig. 8.19 (below) Land use: Grange Farm.

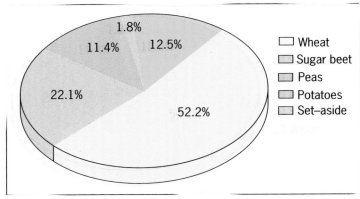

Fig. 8.20 Combine harvesting at Grange Farm

Potatoes, sugar beet, wheat and peas are grown on an eight-year cycle (rotation) (Fig. 8.18). No one crop is grown in the same field in successive years. This helps to maintain the soil's fertility and ensures that any weeds and pests associated with particular crops are controlled.

Grange Farm is typical of arable farming in much of eastern England today: it is a large-scale, highly efficient farm, organised on scientific and business principles. We call this type of farming **agribusiness.** Grange Farm belongs to a group of seven farms which cover nearly 2500 hectares in North Lincolnshire. The farms belong to a single family business, though each one is run separately. Mark Worrall is in charge of Grange Farm. He is a professional farm manager and agriculturalist and is responsible for 272 hectares of arable land, six full-time labourers and various casual workers employed at different times of the year.

Being part of a large business enterprise gives Grange Farm several advantages. The main one is that it can reduce the costs of its inputs. For instance, buying fertiliser and pesticides (agro-chemicals) in bulk is cheaper; machinery can be shared between the seven farms; the cost of administration can be dealt with at a central office, and so on. We refer to these advantages of size as **economies of scale**.

Cultivation at Grange Farm is intensive. Crop yields are high partly because of the favourable climate and soils, and partly because inputs of agro-chemicals (fertilisers and pesticides) and capital equipment, such as tractors, combines, grain driers, refrigerated stores, etc., are high.

Government policies can also influence farming (Table 8.7). In the European Union (known as the Economic Comunity before 1993) the choice of crops and methods of farming often depends on subsidies from the Common Agricultural Policy (CAP) and individual governments. For example, shortages of vegetable oil in the EU in the 1970s led to CAP subsidies for growing oilseed rape. As a result, production grew rapidly and now oilseed rape is a familiar crop in the British countryside. The CAP also guarantees to buy cereals, potatoes, sugar beet and peas at a given minimum price. This has encouraged farmers to produce more and more, thus creating huge food surpluses in the EU in the 1980s. We can see one effect of this at Grange Farm. Some land is 'set-aside' and is not used for cropping. By paying farmers to take arable land out of cultivation the EU hopes to reduce food surpluses. Overall, 18 per cent of the arable land at Grange Farm and its 'sister' farms is in 'set-aside'.

The choice of crops and methods of cultivation at Grange Farm are also affected by the location of markets. Several crops are grown under contract to large food companies such as Birds Eye. These companies often insist on strict conditions for cultivation (e.g. inputs of fertiliser, types of seed, previous crops, etc.) as well as crop quality.

There are 32 hectares of vining peas grown under contract to Birds Eye on Grange Farm simply because Birds Eye have a freezing plant nearby at Hull (Fig.8.21). This means that peas can be delivered to the plant within 40 minutes of picking. Sugar beet, also grown under contract, is sent to the sugar refinery at York. Wheat is sent to Brigg for milling as animal feed, and to Gainsborough for milling for biscuits and bread. Some wheat is also exported through the Humber port of Immingham. Potatoes are grown on contract to a large food processing firm at Hornsea in East Yorkshire. However, the bulk of the potato crop is kept in a huge refrigerated store on the farm, and sold direct to wholesalers and supermarkets when prices are favourable. Finally, pigs are sent to a bacon factory at Malton in North Yorkshire, which supplies Tesco and Safeway supermarkets.

Table 8.7 The Common Agricultural Policy (CAP)

The Common Agriculture policy covers the countries of the European Union. It aims to ensure:

1. A fair standard of living to farmers.
2. Reasonable prices for consumers.
3. Stable food supplies.
4. Stable food prices.
5. Increases in productivity through technical progress.

The policy includes:

Intervention buying: to keep prices high, the CAP buys produce which does not reach a minimum target price, thus giving farmers a guaranteed market for their crops. In the past this has created large food surpluses.

Grants: in upland areas (less favoured areas) grants are given for each head of livestock to offset the higher costs of production. Grants are also available for farm modernisation, conservation, converting farmland to woodland, and investment in off-land enterprises such as tourism, golf courses, etc.

Set-aside: farmers are paid to remove (set-aside) either 15 or 18 per cent of their arable land from cultivation for at least five years. The land may be left fallow, planted with trees, or put to non-agricultural use.

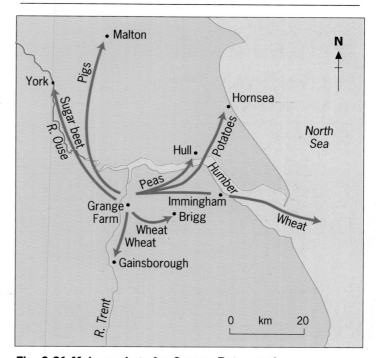

Fig. 8.21 Main markets for Grange Farm products.

EXERCISES

12 Study Figures 8.18 and 8.20. Suggest how the size and shape of fields assist the use of machinery on the farm. What other feature of Figure 8.20 helps the use of machinery?

These food chains tell us that agribusiness in general, and Grange Farm in particular, are part of an integrated food system, which extends all the way from agricultural suppliers to food manufacturers and super-markets.

CASE STUDY

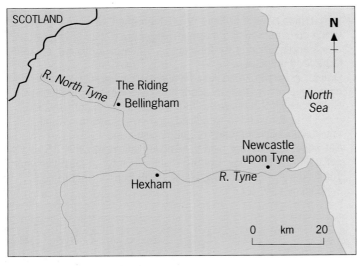

Fig. 8.22 Location of The Riding.

Fig. 8.23 The Riding.

8.10 Hill farming in the UK

The Riding is a hill farm in the North Pennines in Northumberland (Fig.8.22) Covering 385 hectares, the farm extends from the flood plain of the River North Tyne on to the surrounding moorland (Fig.8.24). High precipitation, cool summers and poor soils place severe limits on upland farms such as The Riding (Table 8.8).

Table 8.8 The Riding: physical geography

Altitude (m)	110 – 300
Mean July temperature (°C)	13.7
Mean annual precipitation (mm)	900
Growing season	May to September
Soils	Poor: acidic, clayey and peaty. Better quality, sandy soils in the valley bottom.

Like most farms in highland Britain, The Riding specialises in livestock, in this case lambs and calves. About 950 lambs a year are produced and 'finished' (i.e. fattened for market) on the farm. Given the size of the farm, this is a large number. Ultra-sound scanning makes this possible. It tells the farmer which ewes are carrying one, two or three lambs. As a result he can feed the right amount of food and extra nutrients to each ewe. Around one hundred calves are also reared each year for beef. All of the lambs and calves are sold to a farm co-operative near Newcastle-upon-Tyne. Wool from the ewes provides additional income.

Farming systems in the uplands are extensive (Fig. 8.26). At The Riding the poor-quality grazing supports sheep densities of only 3 to 4 per hectare. Inputs of chemical fertiliser are low. Indeed the farm is largely self-sufficient. All winter feed (hay, silage, turnips, barley) is grown on the farm (Fig. 8.27). There has been a farm on the site for at least 800 years, although there have been many changes over this time. The Riding is an example of a sustainable farm system.

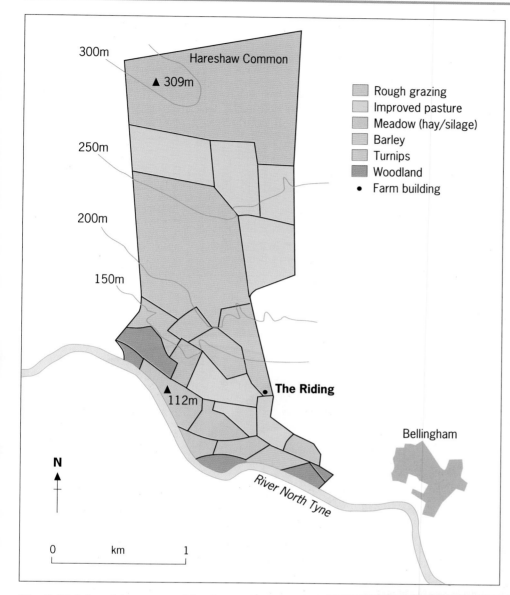

Fig. 8.24 (above) Lay-out and land use: The Riding.

Rough grazing
Improved pasture
Meadow (hay/silage)
Barley
Turnips
Woodland
• *Farm building*

Hareshaw Common
▲ 309m
300m
250m
200m
150m
▲ 112m
The Riding
Bellingham
River North Tyne
N
0 km 1

EXERCISES

14a Study Figure 8.24 and suggest reasons for the location of hay, silage, barley and turnips on the farm.
b* Describe the location of The Riding's farm buildings in relation to the farm's area. What advantages does this location have?
c* Suggest the possible advantages of using contract labour rather than full-time labour.

EXERCISES

15a Trace an outline sketch of the main features in Figure 8.23. On your outline show the main types of land use (i.e. rough grazing, meadow, improved pasture, and woodland)
b* Using the evidence of your outline sketch and Figure 8.24 describe and explain how land use is influenced by slope and altitude.

Fig. 8.25 (below) Sheep shearing, The Riding.

The Riding is a tenant farm run by a manager, Mr Lurati. He is the only full-time worker. Until 1979 there were three full-time workers. Today Mr Lurati gets around the farm on a four-wheeler motor bike. This has enabled him to run the farm by himself. At busy times like sheep clipping, dipping and harvesting, contract labour is also used.

We often describe hill farming as marginal. This means that it is barely profitable. The Common Agricultural Policy helps farmers in 'less favoured areas' like the North Pennines by giving subsidies for each

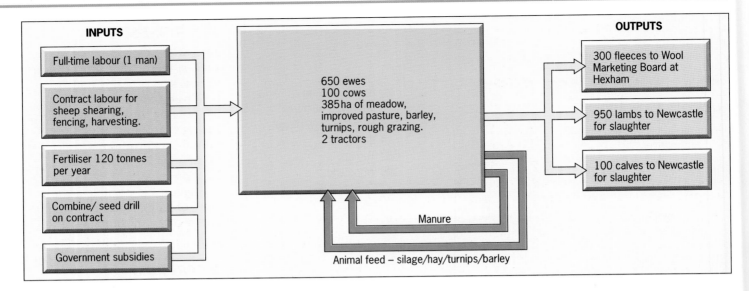

Fig. 8.26 The Riding: farm system.

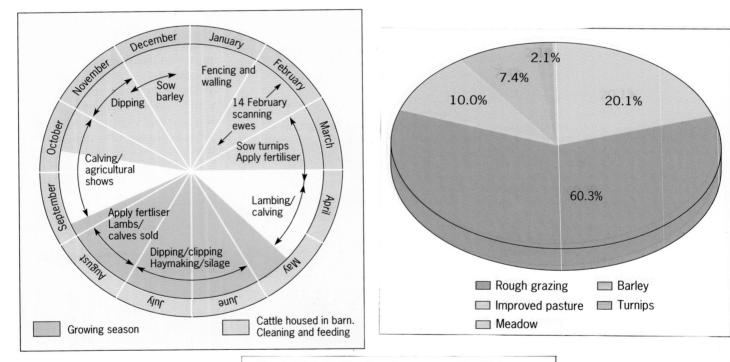

Fig. 8.27 (left) The farming year at The Riding.

Fig. 8.28 (right) Land use: The Riding.

EXERCISES

16 Read the sections on Grange Farm and The Riding. Explain how these factors:
• physical environment • scale, • markets • government policies influence the choice of farm enterprise and farming methods.

head of livestock Table 8.7). Without these payments many hill farms in the EC could not survive. Grants are also available for woodland planting, land drainage, stonewalling, etc., all of which are taken up by The Riding.

8.11 Horticulture in the Netherlands

Horticulture is the intensive cultivation of high-value crops such as fruit, vegetables, flowers, bulbs and garden shrubs. It is a major branch of agriculture in the Netherlands. Although horticulture occupies only five per cent of the Netherlands' farmed area, it accounts for one quarter of the value of all Dutch agricultural exports. Its main markets are the EC (particularly Germany) and North America.

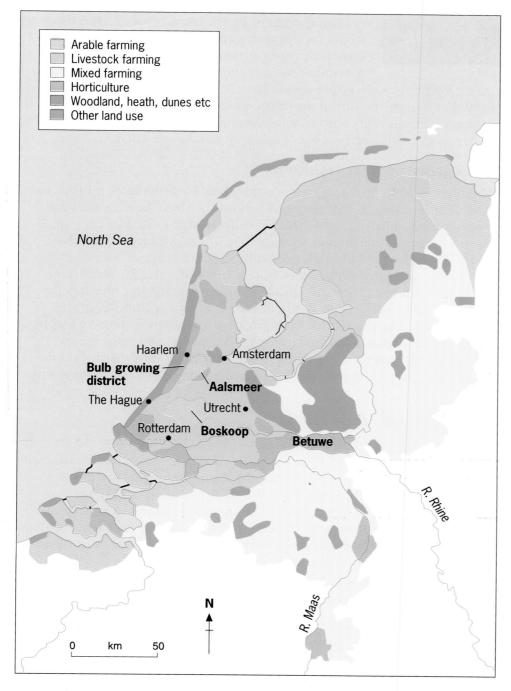

Fig. 8.29 Distribution of types of agriculture in the Netherlands.

Arable farming
Livestock farming
Mixed farming
Horticulture
Woodland, heath, dunes etc
Other land use

North Sea

Haarlem
Amsterdam
Bulb growing district
Aalsmeer
The Hague
Utrecht
Rotterdam **Boskoop**
Betuwe

R. Rhine

R. Maas

N

0   km   50

Fig. 8.30 Bulb fields in the Netherlands.

EXERCISES

17 Study Figure 8.29.
a What physical advantage, also evident in Figure 8.30, do growers have in this area?
b What evidence suggests that farming in the bulb-growing area is intensive?
c* List and explain the possible physical disadvantages for horticulture in this area.

18* Growers still face some physical and economic risks in spite of the artificial physical environment for horticulture in Westland. Can you suggest what these risks might be?

Fig. 8.31 The 'glass city'.

There are a number of specialist horticultural regions in the Netherlands (Fig. 8.29). They include the world-famous bulb fields of the Haarlem area; the glasshouses growing salad crops in the Westland; ornamental trees and shrubs at Boskoop; and orchards in the Betuwe.

Horticulture is both labour intensive and capital intensive. Because of the small size of horticultural holdings (in the crowded western Netherlands small-holdings of less than one hectare are common) intensive methods and reliance on the high value of crops are essential.

The success of Dutch horticulture is due partly to technology and organisation. It is a sophisticated, high-tech type of farming. Growers are supported by scientific research and advisory services. There are many horticultural co-operatives. They provide the credit to growers for materials and horticultural products. Co-operative auctions, where growers can sell their output, exist for many horticultural products. One of these – at Aalsmeer – is the world's largest flower auction.

Bulb growing near Haarlem

The famous bulb-growing area occupies just 3000 hectares on the coast near Haarlem (Fig. 8.31). Situated behind the dune belt, its soils are well-drained, lime rich and ideal for bulb growing. Holdings are small (just 5 hectares on average) though they are much larger than they were 30 years ago. Although the bulb fields are a major tourist attraction in the spring when the flowers are in bloom, the flowers are of secondary interest. They are cut off at an early stage in order not to exhaust the bulbs. Crocus, daffodil, tulip and hyacinth bulbs are exported all over the world. Bulb growing is a labour-intensive business. Demand for labour is particularly high at times of planting, removing flower heads, harvesting, peeling, grading and packing. Local casual labour (including children during school holidays) is used at these busy times.

The Westland: 'glass city'

The Westland is a small, highly – urbanised region between the Hague and the Hook of Holland (Fig. 8.29). Horticulture was initially attracted to the area by its sandy soils. Today there are no longer any physical advantages for horticulture in the Westland: virtually all production takes place in heated glasshouses. The main specialisms are salad crops (tomatoes, lettuce, cucumbers), cut flowers and pot plants. Capital investment is very high. Heating, ventilation, humidity, watering and fertilising are computer controlled. Even the soils are often artificial! The average size of each holding is barely one hectare. None the less, because of the intensity of production such small holdings are profitable

Table 9.1 The aims of the Self-Help project

- to make the region self-sufficient in food production, (after drought in the 1980s had forced the people to depend on food aid).
- to make farming **sustainable**, so that it no longer harmed the environment.
- to develop irrigation (Fig.9.10). This would give higher crop yields, two or more crops a year, and widen the choice of crops to include fruit and vegetables. The last would improve people's diets and provide money through cash sales.
- to use the local farmers' knowledge and skills. Thus when the project ended it was hoped that farmers would be able to maintain the improvements themselves.
- to make a start on the long-term improvement of the environment. Measures were taken to reduce soil erosion, stop overgrazing, and encourage reafforestation (Figs. 9.8, 9.9, 9.11).

Fig. 9.10 Making irrigation channels in Adami Tulu.

The development project

In 1987 a four-year aid project, designed to improve farming in Adami Tulu began. The project was funded by an Irish charity called Self-Help working in partnership with the Ethiopian government and the local farmers. Poverty and environmental degradation were the two most urgent problems which had to be tackled (Fig. 9.6). The project adopted a low-cost, low-technology approach. Table 9.1.

Results

By 1991 most of the project's aims had been achieved. New varieties of seed were introduced and proved popular among farmers. As a result crop yields increased greatly. Farmers began to fence off their pasture-lands to provide forage for livestock in the dry season and prevent over-grazing. They also planted hundreds of thousands of trees for firewood and as shelter belts to protect soils from erosion. Tree nurseries and a research centre for fruit and vegetables were set up, and 38 hectares of farmland irrigated. Eventually this will rise to 200 hectares. Thanks to irrigation, fruit and vegetables are now produced. There is a ready market in the capital, Addis Ababa, which is linked to Adami Tulu by a 150 kilometre tarmac road. Several flour mills for grinding cereals have been built and the number of ponds and boreholes has been increased. The ponds provide water in the dry season, extend the growing period, and help farmers to overcome drought. Boreholes provide clean drinking water. Because water is more available it also makes the lives of women easier. Traditionally, women have been responsible not only for cooking, but also the laborious task of carrying water. (Fig.9.7).

Fig. 9.11 Tree planting in Adami Tulu.

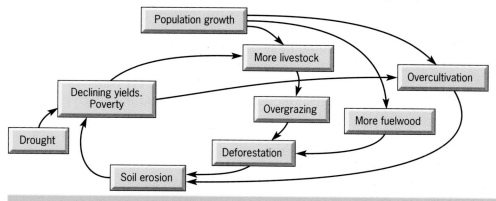

Fig. 9.12 Population growth, poverty and environmental degradation

---

EXERCISES

3 Study Figure 9.12
a Explain how •reafforestation • fencing-off pasture • irrigation and using improved varieties of seed can break the vicious circle in Figure 9.12.
b* Even with the improvements such as reafforestation, irrigation and fencing of pastures, the farming system in Figure 9.12 is likely to be unsustainable in the long term. Can you explain why?

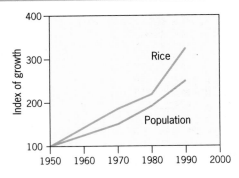

Fig. 9.13 Population growth and rice production in India: 1950-91

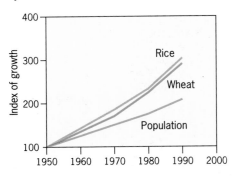

Fig. 9.14 World population growth compared with wheat and rice production: 1950-91.

EXERCISES

4 Study Figure 9.14.
a How do you think the increase in rice production in the world and the growth of population are related?
b Millions of people still suffer food shortages and famine in spite of the increase in production shown in Figure 9.14. Can you suggest reasons for this?

9.3 High-tech change: the green revolution

In the last forty years, high yielding varieties (HYVs) of rice and wheat have been introduced into many economically developing countries. The resulting increase in food production has been dramatic (Fig.9.13). This innovation has become known as the green revolution. Plant breeders in the Philippines and Mexico developed HYVs which then spread rapidly to many parts of the economically developing world (especially Asia) in the 1960s and 1970s (Fig.9.15). For example, India, which until the 1960s had suffered frequent food shortages, became self-sufficient in cereals. As well as increased output, the green revolution brought other benefits to farmers. Crop yields became more reliable and the faster maturing HYVs allowed more than one crop a year to be grown. And because the HYVs gave more food per hectare, farmers could use more of their land for other crops such as vegetables.

Despite its successes, the green revolution has not benefited everyone. One drawback of the higher yielding varieties of rice is that they need irrigation. This is a problem because many of the poorest parts of the world (such as Ethiopia) depend on rain-fed agriculture. HYVs also rely on chemical fertilisers and pesticides which are often unavailable (or unaffordable) to peasant farmers. Finally, farmers adopting HYVs must buy seed every year as the seed from these cereals is infertile.

Traditional wet rice cultivation in East Asia

The green revolution has enabled continuous cropping of rice and has replaced traditional wet rice farming in large parts of East Asia. But is this an improvement on the traditional farming systems?

For hundreds of years wet rice cultivation in China and Japan has been highly successful (Fig.9.16; Fig.9.17). It is a sustainable farming system: in balance with the environment and providing an adequate diet for millions of people. Traditional wet rice cultivation is based on small farms and plentiful supplies of labour. It is highly intensive. As a result yields per hectare are high, and support rural population densities which are among the highest in the world.

The basis of wet rice farming is careful management of water. Rice is cultivated in tiny fields (*padis*) surrounded by earth embankments which keep the water in when the fields are flooded. Rice seedlings are planted by hand in nursery beds, in damp, carefully prepared soil. When they are around 30 centimetres tall they are transplanted into the flooded fields (Fig. 9.16). The fields remain flooded until a few weeks before harvesting, when they are drained. The land is then used for other crops. All of this takes a great deal of labour, but gives overall food yields similar to HYVs.

This traditional farming system is known as a **polyculture** (Fig. 9.16). This means that several different crops are grown, including vegetables and mulberries (for silk worms). Nothing is wasted.

Fig. 9.15 Transplanting high yielding rice, Java.

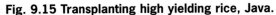

9.8 Soil erosion in the UK

Soil erosion is the removal of top soil by water and wind faster than it can be replaced by natural processes. It is a worldwide problem, found wherever farming occurs. In the UK, soil erosion is most severe in eastern England. In this mainly arable farming region, an average of 20 tonnes of soil per hectare is lost each year. These losses are very serious. In just a few years, erosion can destroy soils which have taken thousands of years to develop.

Causes of soil erosion

In nature the soil is usually covered with vegetation. Plants provide a protective cover, shielding the soil from erosion by wind and rain. Their roots also bind the soil together. Cultivation removes this protective cover, exposing the soil to erosion. For example, ploughing up the natural grasslands of the Great Plains of the USA led to massive wind erosion in the 1930s. So bad was the erosion that this region became known as the 'dust bowl' and huge areas of farmland were abandoned.

Lack of plant cover may occur not just through cultivation but because of overgrazing and deforestation. Both are common causes of soil erosion in the economically developing world (Figs. 9.8, 9.9).

Other causes of soil erosion include cultivating steep hillslopes and ploughing up and down (rather than across) them. In these circumstances each furrow acts as a drainage channel, greatly increasing the rate of erosion. Wheelings (tracks made in fields by farm machinery) create similar channels and erosion problems. Cultivating land with heavy machinery compresses (compacts) the soil – damaging its natural drainage and increasing run-off and erosion. Finally, overcultivation exhausts the soil and removes most of the humus which binds the soil particles together. The use of chemical fertilisers has a similar effect. Without humus, the topsoil degrades into tiny, loose particles which are easily removed by wind and rain.

Types of soil erosion

There are two main agents of soil erosion: water and wind. Water erosion is the main problem in the UK, especially in autumn and winter. Rain runs off the surface carrying with it particles of soil, as well as seeds and fertilisers. As the water runs off the land it is concentrated in channels (Fig 9.33). The smaller channels (rills) are not usually a problem for farmers. They can be easily ploughed-out. However, larger gullies may develop which cannot be crossed by farm machinery (Fig.9.35). The problem is particularly severe on steeply sloping fields.

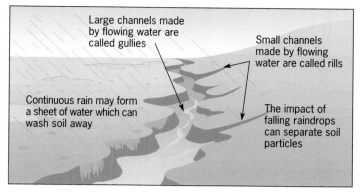

Large channels made by flowing water are called gullies

Small channels made by flowing water are called rills

Continuous rain may form a sheet of water which can wash soil away

The impact of falling raindrops can separate soil particles

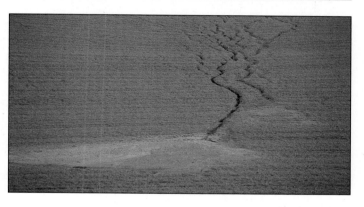

Fig 9.33 (top) Different types of water erosion.

Fig.9.34 (middle) A landscape vulnerable to soil erosion.

Fig. 9.35 (base) Soil erosion and gullying, Nottinghamshire.

> ## EXERCISES
> **13** Study Figure 9.34.
> **a** Suggest possible reasons why the landscape in Figure 9.34 is at risk from soil erosion.
> **b** Describe and explain the types of soil erosion that might take place.

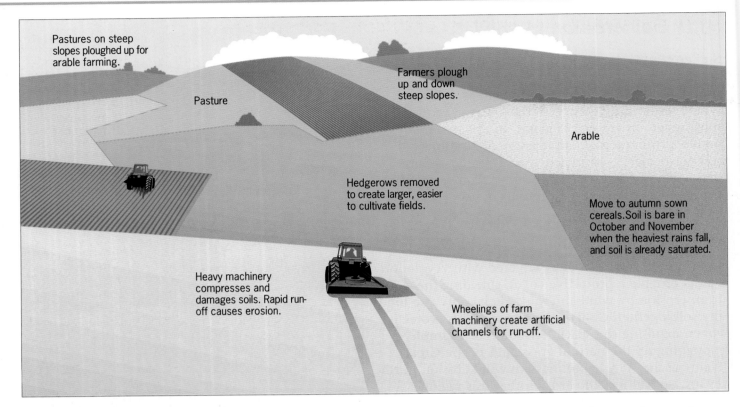

Pastures on steep slopes ploughed up for arable farming.

Pasture

Farmers plough up and down steep slopes.

Arable

Hedgerows removed to create larger, easier to cultivate fields.

Move to autumn sown cereals. Soil is bare in October and November when the heaviest rains fall, and soil is already saturated.

Heavy machinery compresses and damages soils. Rapid run-off causes erosion.

Wheelings of farm machinery create artificial channels for run-off.

Fig. 9.37 A landscape vulnerable to soil erosion.

EXERCISES

14* Trace the outline of Figure 9.37 and modify the farming landscape to reduce the risk of soil erosion. Add notes to your sketch explaining the effects of the changes you have made.

Wind erosion in the UK is a more localised problem. Light, sandy and peaty soils are most at risk, for example, the Vale of York, the Fens in Cambridgeshire and Lincolnshire, and the Breckland in Norfolk.

Early spring, when soils begin to dry out and winds are strong is the most hazardous time (Fig.9.36). Tiny soil particles are lifted into the air and may be carried long distances. Coarser particles are either bounced along (saltation) or roll along the surface (creep).

The effects of soil erosion

Soil erosion not only creates problems on the farm but it also affects a wider area. Apart from the loss of soil, erosion also decreases soil fertility and crop yields thus increasing the farmer's costs of production. For example, seeds may be washed or blown away; roads and drains blocked by eroded soil; and crops sand-blasted by the wind, or smothered by wind-blown material. Off the farm, soil erosion increases the silt load of streams and rivers. As waters become muddy, aquatic plants, insects and fish may disappear. However, farmers can take measures to protect soils from erosion. (Table 9.3 lists some of these.)

Table 9.3 Methods of protecting the soil from erosion in the UK

Contour ploughing	Ploughing across slopes (Contour ploughing) .
Use of machinery	Avoid cultivating wet soils with heavy machinery.
Cover crops	Keep fields partly covered with some crops or crop residues left after harvest.
Wind breaks	Plant trees and hedges to protect the soil from strong winds. Lines of trees provide shelter for up to ten times their height.
Strip cropping	Grow several different crops in one field in strips. The crops ripen at different times so there is always some crop cover to give protection.
Crop rotations	Build up the soil's fertility and its organic content.
Convert arable to pasture	Pasture gives a one hundred per cent plant cover. Soil erosion is minimal.
Plant fewer autumn cereals	If cereals are planted in spring, stubble and plant residues can be left in fields throughout the winter, thus reducing rates of water and wind erosion.

9.9 Summary: Agriculture: problems and change

Generalisations	Detail
There are both high- and low-tech approaches to increasing agricultural production in economically less developed countries.	• In Adami Tulu a low-tech aid project designed to increase food production and improve the environment has been successful. • The green revolution is a high-tech approach to increasing food production. It has increased food output significantly in the economically developing world. However, many small farmers, and many areas in the economically developing world have not benefited.
Low-tech improvements in agriculture in the economically developing world are likely to be more successful than high-tech ones.	• Low-tech improvements are affordable to poor peasant farmers. The use of simple technology allows the skills of local people to be used. • High-tech improvements are expensive and tend to benefit the rich more than the poor.
There are chronic shortages of food in many of the poorest economically developing countries.	• Food shortages stem from drought, rapid population growth, civil wars, etc. In times of famine many poor countries have to rely on food aid from the economically developed world.
Population growth and agriculture have contributed to environmental degradation in the economically developing world.	• Rapid population growth has meant extending and intensifying agriculture to increase food production. This has put the environment under pressure in many parts of the economically developing world. The result is overcultivation, overgrazing, deforestation, soil erosion, etc.
The Common Agriculture Policy has caused economic and environmental problems in the EU.	• The CAP has encouraged the intensification and extension of farming. The result has been huge food surpluses and environmental degradation (destruction of habitats, pollution, soil erosion, etc.). • In the 1980s and 1990s the CAP introduced measures to reduce surpluses (e.g. set-aside) and improve the environment (ESAs, woodland and hedgerow planting, nitrate-sensitive areas etc.).
Soil erosion invariably accompanies cultivation.	• Soil erosion is widespread in the UK and especially in the arable areas of eastern England. Wind and rain are responsible for most soil erosion. • Soil erosion not only results in the loss of topsoil, it increases the costs of cultivation and reduces crop yields.
There is a range of conservation measures which can significantly reduce rates of soil erosion.	• Wind erosion can be lessened by planting shelter belts. • Strip cropping, the growing of cover crops and leaving crop residues in the fields reduce both wind and water erosion. Contour ploughing helps to conserve soils on hill slopes. • Keeping soils fertile with the use of manure makes soil erosion less likely.

Fig. 9.36 Wind erosion.

10 Industrial activity and location

EXERCISES

1 Study Figures 10.1 – 10.5.
a Identify each of the economic activities.
b State to which of the three main economic sectors each activity belongs.
c Explain why you selected that sector for each activity.

10.1 Introduction

We divide economic activities into three main sectors: **primary**, **secondary** and **tertiary**. The primary sector produces food and raw materials. It includes agriculture, mining and quarrying, fishing and forestry. The secondary sector is manufacturing industry. The tertiary sector is more complicated because it involves many service activities. These range from transport and education, to retailing, banking and tourism.

Fig. 10.1 – 10.5 Economic activities.

10.2 The distribution of industrial activities

From Figure 10.6, you can see that the importance of manufacturing industry varies from one country to another. Manufacturing is least important in the world's poorest countries. For example, economically developing countries in Africa, such as Burundi, Uganda and Malawi, have fewer than five per cent of their working population in manufacturing industry. In contrast, manufacturing employs at least 20 per cent of the working population in economically developed countries.

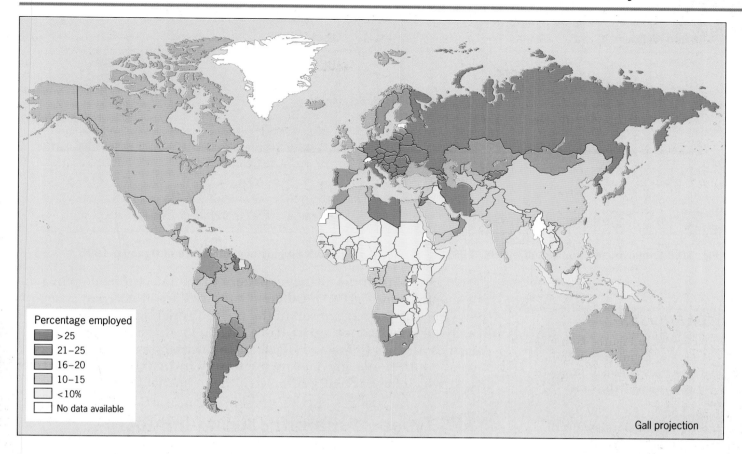

Figure 10.7 explains why the importance of manufacturing varies so much between countries. If we turn the clock back to Europe in the early eighteenth century, we find that most people worked in agriculture. Then, around 1750, a remarkable change began to happen. Industries started to use coal as a source of power; new machines were invented; and manufacturing moved from cottages and workshops to factories. As a result, industrial production increased massively.

We refer to these changes as the **industrial revolution.** The industrial revolution both transformed industry and changed the lives of millions of people as they left farming for the newly built factories in the towns (see Chapter 6).

This so-called industrial phase (Fig.10.7) lasted until the mid-twentieth century. By 1995, much of the economically developed world is in the **post-industrial** period. As manufacturing increases in efficiency and machines replace workers, more and more people move to work in the tertiary sector. At the same time, people become better off, and spend more on services such as health care, leisure, tourism, travel and so on. AS a result more jobs develop in the tertiary sector. Thus, in the UK, as in other economically developed countries, we now live in a world where employment is dominated by service activities (Fig.10.8).

Fig.10.6 (above) Global distribution of employment in manufacturing industry, 1994.

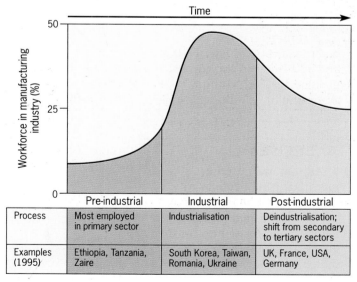

Fig. 10.7 (above) The changing importance of manufacturing industry.

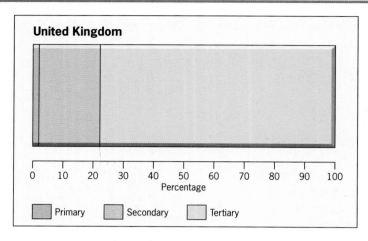

Fig. 10.8 Employment structure of the UK, 1995.

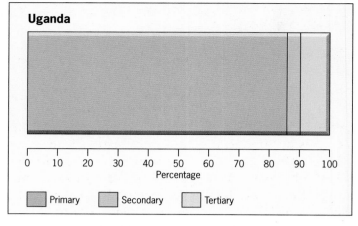

Fig. 10.9 Employment structure of Uganda, 1995.

We can think of the changing pattern of manufacturing employment as a simple cycle (Fig.10.7). Different countries are in different stages of this cycle. The poorest are still in the pre-industrial stage and depend heavily on **subsistence agriculture** (Fig.10.9). In contrast, some countries, such as China and Brazil, are industrialising rapidly. Others, such as South Korea and Taiwan, are **newly industrialising countries** (NICs) which have recently completed the industrial stage.

10.3 Types of manufacturing industry

Manufacturing industries use either raw materials or put together (assemble) parts to make products. Because of the work and materials involved in both types of manufacturing, the final products have **added value.**

Some manufacturing industries simply process raw materials. These industries, which include oil refining and iron making, are known as processing industries. Their main purpose is to supply other manufacturing industries with essential materials. Another group of industries, such as textiles and pottery, use raw materials without any processing to make finished products. Finally, assembly industries buy components (parts) from other firms, and put them together to make a finished product. Motor vehicle manufacture is probably the best-known example of an assembly industry. In the next few pages we shall look at examples of these different types of industry in the UK.

Table 10.1 Matching exercise: manufacturing industries, raw materials and products

Industry	Raw material	Semi-finished product	Finished product
Printing	timber	wood pulp	paper/cardboard
Motor vehicles	cotton	molasses	ethylene
Aerospace	bauxite	alumina	syrup
Fashion	sugar cane	refined oil	aluminium
Construction	iron ore	pig iron	sheet steel
Paint	crude oil	yarn	concrete
Food processing	limestone	cement	cloth

EXERCISES

2 Compare Figures 10.8 and 10.9 and comment on the differences between the two employment structures.

3a Locate the following countries in an atlas: Brazil, Sudan, Mali, Kazakhstan, Poland, France, Libya, Chile, Mexico and China.
b With reference to Figure 10.7 decide which stage of development (pre-industrial, industrial, or post-industrial) each country has reached.
c Draw a copy of Figure 10.7 and add labels in the correct position for each country, according to its industrial stage.

EXERCISES

4 All materials used in manufacturing begin as raw materials. Many are processed into semi-finished products before being made into finished goods. Copy Table 10.1 and match the relevant industries with their raw materials, semi-finished and finished products. The first one (printing, pulp, paper, timber.) has been done for you.

10.4 The pottery industry in Stoke-on-Trent

Stoke-on-Trent is a small conurbation of 250 000 people in North Staffordshire (Fig.10.10). Located on a coalfield, it grew in importance after 1750 as the centre of the UK's pottery industry. Stoke-on-Trent has kept its position as the pottery industry's leading centre to the present day. In 1991, 22 600 people worked in the pottery (and other ceramic goods) industry in the UK; 53 per cent of these were in Stoke-on-Trent.

Pottery manufacture has a long history in Stoke-on-Trent. It was first recorded in the fourteenth century, when it was a **cottage industry** (see section 10.10). Large-scale factory production only occurred after 1750. The initial attractions for the industry were local materials, especially clay and coal for firing the kilns. During the eighteenth century, a number of new developments made local materials less important. Ball clay (from Dorset), was used to make earthenware products, and flint and china clay (from Cornwall) were introduced to make porcelain. But, these imported, bulky materials were expensive to transport, especially when overland transport relied on horse-drawn carts and packhorses. This problem was solved in 1777 with the opening of the Trent-Mersey Canal. It then became possible to transport raw materials from Dorset and Cornwall by sea to the Mersey estuary and then by canal to Stoke-on-Trent.

Many of these changes came about with the help of one man, Josiah Wedgwood. He built a new factory, called Etruria, alongside the Trent-Mersey canal in 1769 (Fig.10.11). The Wedgwood works survives today, although it now occupies an edge-of-town site at Barlaston (Fig.10.10).

By the mid-twentieth century, most of the **initial advantages** which first attracted the pottery industry to Stoke-on-Trent had disappeared. Local clays were no longer used, and gas and electricity had replaced coal for firing the kilns. And yet Stoke-on-Trent continues to dominate the UK pottery industry. Why is this? One reason is the difficulty and expense of moving factories and heavy machinery to new locations. Even if this were possible, it would not be worthwhile so long as the factory remained profitable. We call this **industrial inertia.** It is an important influence on industrial location and means that industries tend to stay where they first started.

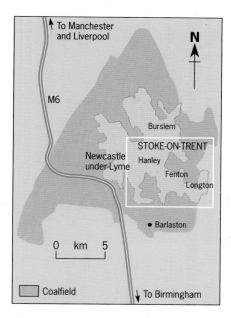

Fig.10.10 (above) Location of Stoke-on-Trent.

Fig. 10.11 (middle) Etruria in the 1850's.

Fig. 10.12 (right) John Tams factory.

Fig.10.13 Location of John Tams production sites and its local suppliers.

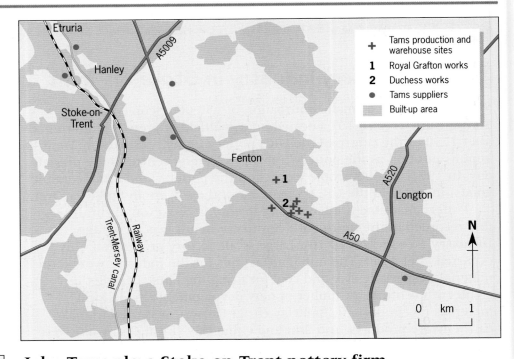

John Tams plc: a Stoke-on-Trent pottery firm

There are other reasons for the survival of the pottery industry in Stoke-on-Trent. We shall illustrate these by looking at a typical pottery firm in the region, John Tams plc. Founded in 1874, John Tams makes earthenware and fine bone china (Royal Grafton and Duchess).

You can see from the systems diagram (Fig.10.14) that few inputs are local materials. Even so, there are advantages to locating in the Stoke region. First, all of John Tams' materials and machinery are obtained from local firms which are specialist suppliers to the pottery industry. These suppliers both find their own basic materials and process them to the pottery makers' demands. Such close links between suppliers and pottery makers are not available in other cities, and are a powerful reason for locating (and remaining) in Stoke-on-Trent. We refer to these links as **external economies.**

Second, Tams employ around 1000 people, most of whom are either skilled or semi-skilled workers. Many skills, such as gilding and decorating china are passed from generation to generation, and are mainly found in the Stoke region. This gives Stoke an added advantage over other regions for pottery manufacture.

Fig. 10.14 John Tams plc; a pottery manufacturing system.

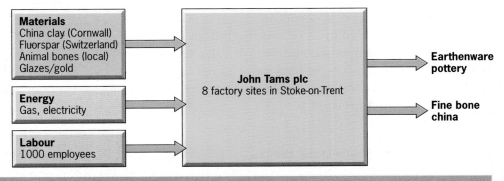

10.5 The UK iron and steel industry

Iron and steel making is an important industry for a modern industrial economy. Many industries, such as car making, construction and engineering use steel as their basic material.

There are three main operations in iron and steel making. First, coking coal and limestone are used to smelt iron ore in a blast furnace to make iron. Second, the iron is refined in a furnace to produce steel. And third, the steel is shaped to make a range of products such as beams, rails, plate, coil and so on.

In a modern integrated iron and steel works, all three operations take place on the same site (Fig.10.16). This helps to cut both transport and fuel costs. For example, molten iron is taken directly from the blast furnace to the steel - making plant. Such integrated iron and steel plants are very large and often occupy sites covering six or seven square kilometres. Large plants are essential if the costs of making steel are to be kept as low as possible. We call the savings associated with large plants, **economies of scale.**

Iron and steel is a heavy industry. Its raw materials are bulky; they are used in very large quantities and are expensive to transport. During manufacture, though, these raw materials lose a lot of their weight. This has had an important effect on the industry's location. In order to keep its transport costs low, the iron and steel industry has always located as close as possible to its materials. Thus, for most of the nineteenth century, iron making located on the coalfields, in regions such as South Wales and the West Midlands. Later, with the discovery of iron ore deposits in Lincolnshire and the East Midlands, plants such as Scunthorpe and Corby were built on the orefields (Fig.10.15).

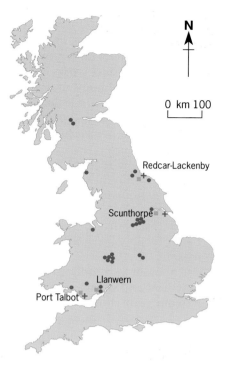

■ Integrated iron and steel works

+ Deep-water teminal for ore and coal

● Works making steel products (e.g. tubes, strip etc.)

Fig. 10.15 Distribution of the UK iron and steel industry, 1995.

Fig. 10.16 A modern, integrated iron and steel works.

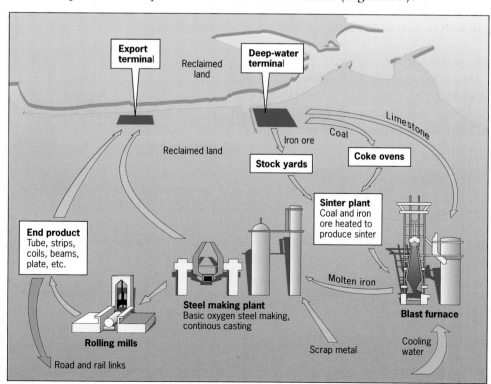

159

EXERCISES

6 Figure 10.17 shows four possible locations (A-D) for a new iron and steel works. The works will use imported iron ore and coal, local limestone, and employ around 3000 people. It will need a flat site covering 6 km².

a In 1850 the region had a thriving iron industry. Explain why the industry developed here.

b Suggest which location (A-D) it probably occupied, giving reasons.

c Choose a location for the new iron and steel works. Explain your choice.

Since 1945, the industry has relied increasingly on imported materials. This has led to a movement to coastal locations. Here imported iron ore and coking coal, brought in by 200 000 tonne bulk carriers, can be processed most cheaply.

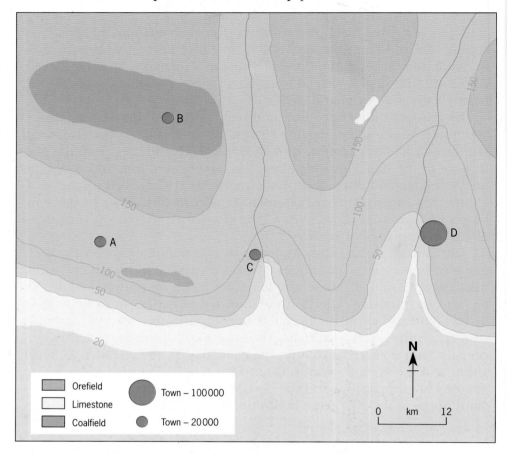

Fig. 10.17 Locating an iron and steel works.

CASE STUDY

10.6 The Redcar-Lackenby iron and steelworks

Redcar-Lackenby on Teesside is one of four integrated iron and steelworks operated by British Steel in the UK. Iron and steel making started on Teesside in the mid-nineteenth century. The initial advantages were iron deposits in the nearby Cleveland Hills, and coking coal from the Durham coalfield (Fig.10.18). In 1995, with the exception of limestone, the Teesside iron and steel industry no longer uses local materials.

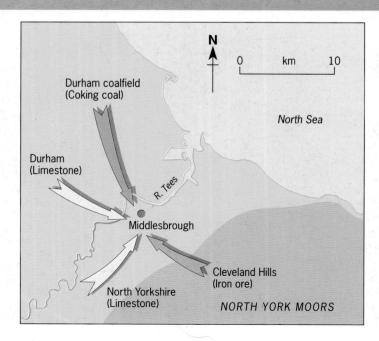

Fig. 10.18 Iron and steel making on Teesside.

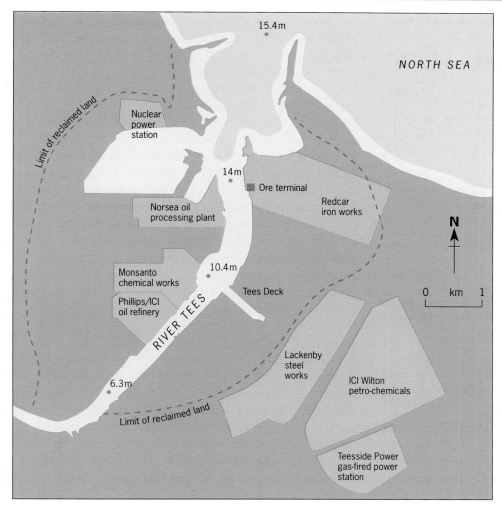

15.4m

NORTH SEA

Limit of reclaimed land

Nuclear power station

14m

Ore terminal

Redcar iron works

Norsea oil processing plant

N

Monsanto chemical works

10.4m

Tees Deck

0   km   1

Phillips/ICI oil refinery

RIVER TEES

Lackenby steel works

6.3m

ICI Wilton petro-chemicals

Limit of reclaimed land

Teesside Power gas-fired power station

Fig. 10.19 (left) The heavy industrial complex at the mouth of the River Tees.

Fig. 10.20 (below) Redcar-Lackenby steel works at the mouth of the River Tees, looking south.

Table 10.2 Advantages of the Tees estuary for the location of heavy industries

Industrial sites	Large expanses of flat, reclaimed land. Ideal for heavy, space-using industries such as Redcar-Lackenby iron and steel works, ICI Wilton (petrochemicals), Monsanto (chemicals), North Tees oil refinery (Phillips), Hartlepool nuclear power station, Teesside gas power station (Wilton).
Access to tidewater	Deep - water channel in the Tees estuary allows bulk carriers (up to 200 000 tonnes) to bring oil, iron ore and coal to heavy processing industries. Refined oil products and steel are exported by sea.
Remoteness	The Teesside industrial complex is near the mouth of the river and downwind of the main urban areas. This location helps reduce the risk of accident and minimises air pollution.
Access to water	Water is extracted from the river for industrial processes, while polluted water can be discharged into the estuary.

EXERCISES

8* Heavily industrialised estuaries may have disadvantages for people living nearby and for wildlife. Write about some of these possible disadvantages.

Meanwhile, during the 1960's and 1970's many traditional steel - making centres closed down. Most of these centres had one feature in common: they were located inland. Closure took place because it was simply too expensive to transport imported iron ore and coal from the coast.

Geography has been important for the survival of iron and steel making on Teesside. As the city is located on the deep water estuary of the River Tees, its industries could easily switch to importing materials. Thus, in 1976, a new iron works with its own deep water terminal (capable of handling 200 000 - tonne bulk carriers) was built at Redcar (Fig.10.14).

The Tees estuary has other advantages for iron and steel making and for heavy processing industries like petrochemicals and oil refining (Table 10.2 and Fig.10.19). Most important are the large areas of flat, reclaimed land near the river mouth. As a result, the Tees estuary now has the largest single concentration of heavy industry in the UK.

Redcar is the iron-making side of the UK's largest integrated iron and steel works. Iron ore imported from Australia, Canada, West Africa and Brazil is stockpiled on site. Coal from Australia and the USA is made into coke and, along with limestone, is fed into Europe's largest blast furnace. The molten iron is then taken by rail the short distance to the steel plant at Lackenby. Here, it is converted into steel slabs using the latest basic oxygen furnaces and continuous casting techniques. Finally, the steel slabs are shaped into finished beams and steel coil. Total output from the Redcar-Lackenby plant is around 3.5 million tonnes of steel a year. Steel products are exported by sea from Tees Dock, while most steel for the UK market is transported by rail.

10.7 Car manufacturing industry

Car manufacturing is an assembly industry. Components such as engines, radiators, spark plugs, windscreens, seats etc., made by hundreds of different firms, are put together at an assembly plant. We refer to this system as horizontal organisation (Fig.10.21).

Car making is a leading industry in the developed world (Fig.10.22). Although production is growing rapidly in some economically developing countries, like Brazil and China, in the mid-1990s nine out of every ten cars were still made in the developed world.

Huge **transnational corporations** (TNCs) dominate world car production. Many of these companies, e.g. General Motors, Ford, Toyota, Nissan, are household names. TNCs operate assembly plants and component factories in many different countries. In the next section we shall look at the most international of all motor vehicle TNCs: Ford.

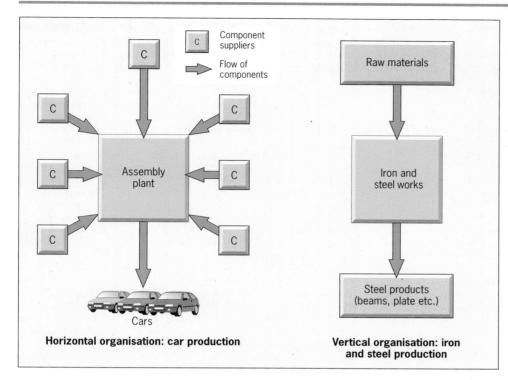

Horizontal organisation: car production

Vertical organisation: iron and steel production

Component suppliers

Flow of components

EXERCISES

9a Study Figure 10.21. Describe how the organisation of the car industry differs from the iron and steel industry.
b* Suggest possible reasons why it is an advantage for component suppliers in the car industry to locate close to assembly plants.

Fig. 10.21 (above) Horizontal and vertical types of organisation.

Fig. 10.22 (below) World car production, 1995.

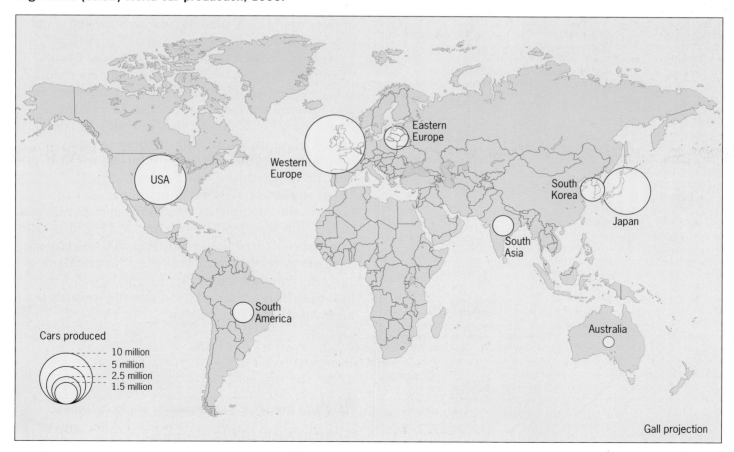

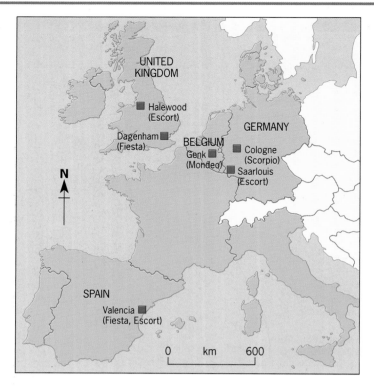

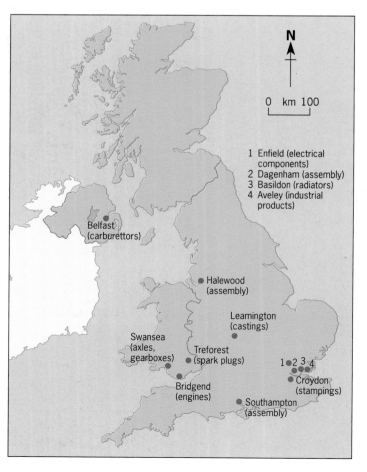

Integration and globalisation: Ford Motors

Ford is an American TNC with its headquarters in Detroit. After General Motors, it is the world's second largest car manufacturer. In the 1900s, Ford first developed the mass production of vehicles using moving assembly lines.

The company then opened its first overseas plant in Manchester, UK, in 1911. In 1995, it had assembly plants throughout the USA and the EU (Fig.10.23), as well as in Mexico, South America, East Asia, South-east Asia and Australia. In total, Ford employed 350 000 people worldwide. Before the end of the twentieth century Ford aims to build assembly plants in China and India.

In Europe, Ford's operations are fully integrated. In fact, it has a common car range for the whole of Europe. For example, the plants at Dagenham and Valencia (Figs.10.23, 10.24) produce all of the Fiestas sold in Europe, while Halewood and Saarlouis plants make Escorts. What advantage does this policy have? Essentially, it lowers costs and helps to make Ford more competitive. By concentrating on just a few models for the entire European market, Ford can make a large number of cars. This is important because the costs of developing new models (research, design, new machine tools etc.) are enormous. For example, in 1995 Ford decided to build a new Jaguar car at Coventry. The cost of developing this new model will be around £500 million. Overall expenses are also lowered if a factory specialises in making a single model or component (e.g. Ford's Bridgend engine plant in South Wales). These savings, or economies of scale, are vital to the success of large-volume car producers like Ford.

In the next few years Ford aims to go even further and integrate its operations at a global scale. In fact, the Mondeo is Ford's first truly 'global' car: it is manufactured worldwide and sold in markets in many different countries. Other car companies such as General Motors, Toyota and Nissan are following Ford's example and moving towards the **globalisation** of production.

Fig. 10.23 (top) Ford's car assembly plants in Europe.

Fig. 10.24 (left) Ford's UK operations.

10.8 The UK car industry

The UK car industry, together with the manufacture of car components, employs over 200 000 people. In 1995, the car industry produced exports worth £7 billion – more than any other manufacturing industry apart from electronics. In fact, most of the world's leading car manufacturers have assembly plants in the UK (Fig.10.25).

The early car industry

The car industry first developed in the early twentieth century in the West Midlands and the South-east. It grew out of related industries such as coach building and bicycles. Labour skills from these industries were easily transferred to car making. In the West Midlands there were also long - established engineering and metal - working industries which supplied components for the new car industry.

Although skilled labour is no longer important, the West Midlands and the South-east remain leading centres of car production (Fig.10.25). The many component suppliers in these regions have a significant locational advantage.

Locational change in the 1960s

In the early 1960s, several new car factories were located in Merseyside and Central Scotland. These regions had no tradition of car making. However, the government believed that the car industry would generate new jobs and economic growth in these less prosperous regions. As a result, the government directed investment to the new assembly plants and away from the West Midlands and the South-east. Not all of the new plants were successful, but Ford's plant at Halewood, and Vauxhall's at Ellesmere Port (both on Merseyside) have survived.

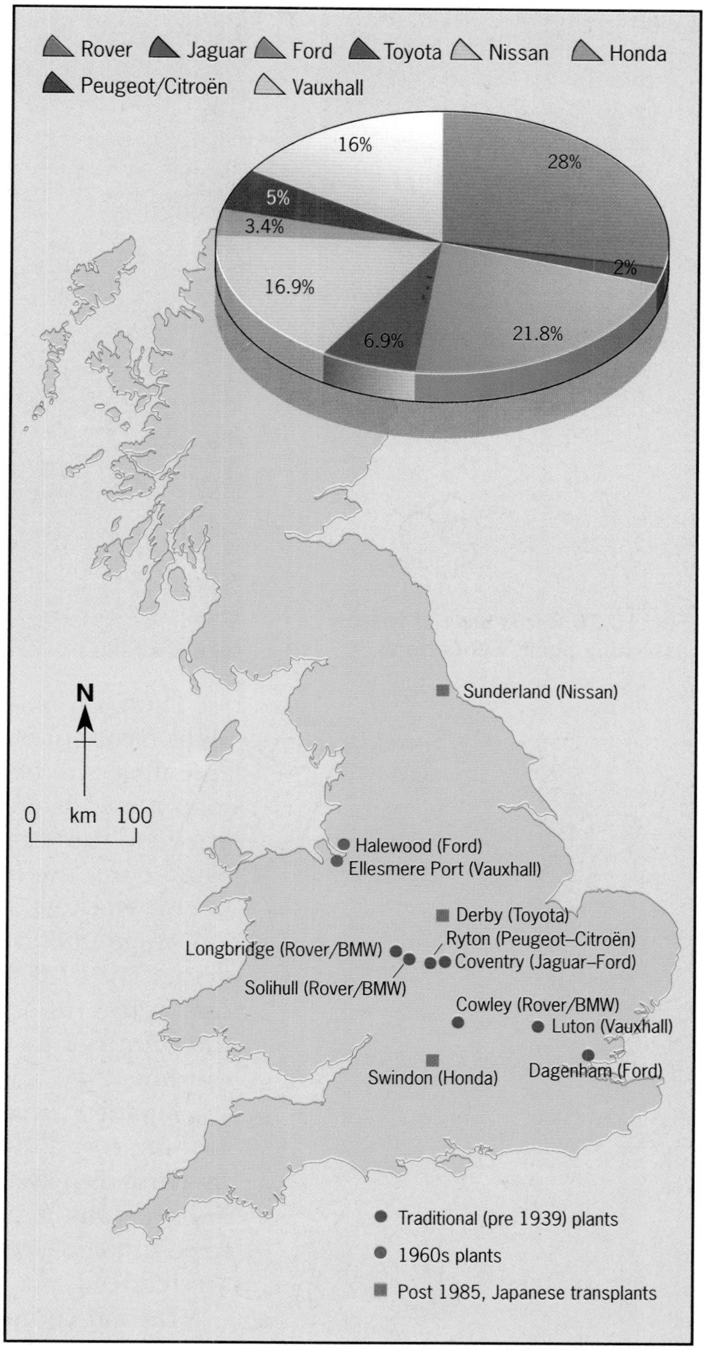

The Japanese drive into the EU

From 1970 to 1985 the UK car industry was in decline. Output fell from 1.6 million cars in 1970, to less than one million in 1982. Workers' strikes were common and a number of foreign firms took over several British manufacturers.

Fig. 10.25 (above) UK car assembly plants and production.

EXERCISES

10 Describe the distribution of car assembly plants in the UK built before 1939 (Figure 10.25). How does it compare with the distribution of assembly plants built since 1960?

EXERCISES

11 Study Figure 10.26. Identify three features of the Nissan site which might explain why Nissan chose this location.

Fig. 10.26 Aerial view of Nissan assembly plant, Sunderland.

Then, in 1984, Nissan chose the UK for its first European assembly plant (**transplant**). Within two years Nissan had begun production on a greenfield site near Sunderland. This was so successful that Nissan was soon joined by Toyota (in Derby) and Honda (in Swindon). The UK provided these Japanese manufacturers with a base from which they could enter the EU market. They were also attracted by the quality of British workers, the lack of competition from British car manufacturers, low wage rates and, in the case of Nissan, £65 million in government grants. By 1995, therefore, Nissan had become the largest exporter of cars in the UK and Japanese transplants accounted for one quarter of the country's total car production - a proportion which will rise to one third by 2000 (Fig.10.25).

Japanese firms not only increased car production in the UK, they also improved quality and introduced new production methods. '**Just-in-time**' is a system where components are supplied to the assembly lines just hours before they are needed. Car makers therefore do not need to keep expensive stocks of components on site. As a result, costs are reduced.

The car components industry received a boost through an agreement that 80 per cent of parts had to be supplied from within the EU. (This avoided the threat that transplants would become 'screwdriver' factories, merely assembling parts imported from Japan). As a result, many Japanese parts manufacturers then followed Nissan, Toyota and Honda to the UK. Ten per cent of Nissan's 204 European suppliers are in the UK. Many located in North-east England and one, Ikeda Hoover (which makes seats), has its factory actually within the Nissan site.

10.9 High - technology industries in the UK

High-technology (high-tech) industries cover a wide range of activities, including micro-electronics, computers, telecommunications, biotechnology, pharmaceuticals and many others. Like iron and steel and car making, high-tech industries need a lot of investment. However, one special feature of high-tech industries is the importance they give to researching and developing new products.

In the UK, around six per cent of manufacturing jobs are in the high-tech sector. In fact, high-tech industries are the UK's leading exporters. In 1994 they exported goods worth £7.5 billion.

However, like car manufacturing, high-tech industry is dominated by TNCs. GlaxoWellcome is a UK-owned company which is a market leader in pharmaceuticals, but the electronics industry in the UK is almost entirely controlled by foreign (mainly US and Japanese) companies. Many of these companies, such as IBM, Motorola, Apple, Mashushita, Fujitsu and Sony are well known.

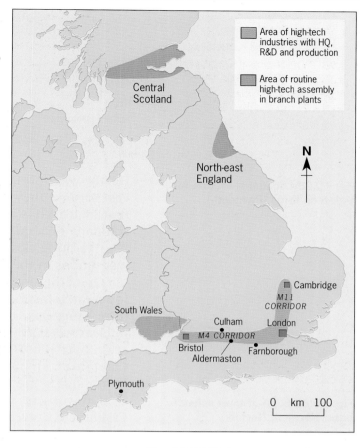

Fig. 10.27 Major concentrations of high-tech industry, UK.

Footloose but not free: the location of high-tech industries

Most high-tech products have relatively low weight and bulk. This means that the cost of transport, both of components for assembly, and of finished products for market, is fairly low. Therefore, compared to iron and steel and pottery, transport is not of such importance to the location of high-tech industries. Similarly, other traditional locational factors, such as supplies of materials and energy, have little importance. Industries, such as high-tech, which are not limited in their choice of location by transport, materials or energy are called **footloose**. Yet, despite having a much freer choice of location than heavy industries, high-tech industries cannot locate anywhere they like.

High-tech location in the UK

The main concentrations of high-tech industries in the UK are found in just a few regions (Fig.10.27). This tells us that there must be locational advantages for high-tech industries in some areas but not in others. In order to explain the distribution in Figure 10.27, we need to understand that high-tech enterprises fall into two types. First, there are those which have their headquarters, research and development (R & D) and manufacturing functions all on the same site. Second, there are high-tech enterprises in the UK which are only involved in manufacturing.

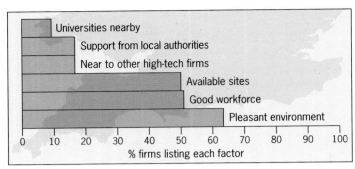

Fig. 10.28 Locational factors for high-tech firms (Plymouth).

Bar chart — % firms listing each factor:
- Universities nearby
- Support from local authorities
- Near to other high-tech firms
- Available sites
- Good workforce
- Pleasant environment

x-axis: 0 10 20 30 40 50 60 70 80 90 100
% firms listing each factor

HQ, R&D and manufacturing functions

As well as semi-skilled production workers the first type of enterprise needs to employ highly trained managers and skilled scientists and technicians to design and develop new products. Because managers and scientists are in short supply, these hightech firms choose to locate in regions with good housing, services and attractive countryside. Of course, there are other locational factors (Fig.10.28). Heathrow airport attracts large numbers of high-tech firms to the South-east because they need good international transport links. Remember that high-tech is a global industry and most firms in the UK have their company headquarters in the USA, Japan, Germany and South Korea. Also, locating close to London gives access to banks and other financial institutions in the City of London which invest in high-tech businesses.

One other important locational factor in the South-east is closeness to research institutions. Firms locating along the M4 corridor benefit from being close to several universities, aircraft research at Farnborough, nuclear weapons research at Aldermaston, and atomic energy research at Culham (Fig.10.27). The main attraction of the M11 corridor is Cambridge; an historic city with good communications with London. Cambridge is the UK's leading high-tech growth centre, employing over 20 000 workers. There is close co-operation between scientists at Cambridge University and high-tech industries in the city. In fact, it was

Fig. 10.29 Edge-of-town science park, Norwich, Norfolk.

one of the Cambridge University colleges which established the UK's first science park. By 1995, many new high-tech factories had located on edge-of-town sites in purpose-built science parks (Fig.10.29). There are now twenty-five such science parks scattered throughout the UK, many closely linked to universities.

Manufacturing only

The second type of high-tech enterprises, which concentrate only on production (branch plants), have different locational needs (Fig.10.27). Branch plants only need to recruit semi-skilled, low-cost labour because they have no headquarter or R & D functions. As a result, since the 1980s many branch plants have located in economically developing countries, such as Thailand and Mexico. Here, labour costs are very low. In the UK, high-tech branch plants owned by foreign TNCs are mostly located in assisted areas (see Chapter 11). These are areas where companies receive government grants. The most popular regions for foreign investment in high-tech industry have been North-east England (see Chapter 11), central Scotland and South Wales. For example, Sony in South Wales, directly employs 3000 people in its factories and indirectly supports a further 9000 in component manufacturers nearby.

Advantages of the UK

US, Japanese and Korean high-tech firms use their factories in the UK as a base for supplying the EU. Another advantage of the UK is its low labour costs compared with its European competitors such as Germany, France, Belgium and the Netherlands.

10.10 Cottage industries and appropriate technology

Most manufacturing industries in economically developed countries are capital intensive, use advanced technology and highly educated labour forces, and take place in purpose-built factories. We have seen that their products are increasingly sold globally.

Similar industries exist in most large cities in economically developing countries. However, much manufacturing here is different. This is because it is usually small-scale, based on simple technology, and uses local materials and traditional skills to produce goods for the local community. Such industries are often located in people's homes in rural areas, or in small workshops in towns. These so-called cottage industries were once common in Europe before the industrial revolution.

Some economically developing countries like China, India and Brazil are building capital - intensive, advanced-technology industries, but most governments and aid organisations do not see these big   projects as the best way forward for the developing world. Industries using advanced technology may bring prestige to the country but they rarely benefit the majority of the people. The most successful schemes are based on low technology, use local materials and traditional skills, and cost relatively little to introduce. They involve the local people who are consulted about their specific needs. We shall now look at two schemes in economically developing countries which are based on these principles and use technology which is appropriate for local people's needs (appropriate technology).

10.11 Making cooking stoves in western Kenya

In 1987 the UK charity Intermediate Technology taught a group of women potters (the Keyo group) in western Kenya (Fig.10.30) how to make the *upesi*, an efficient wood - burning stove. The stove uses less than half the fuelwood of an open fire and it can also burn maize stalks and dry sugar cane. It is also safer and cleaner. The stove is simple and effective and brings benefits to everyone. Because it burns less wood, it saves time collecting fuelwood; it saves money for those who normally buy their fuelwood at the market; and it saves forests and woodlands from destruction. In addition, because the *upesi* produces less smoke than an open fire, it helps to reduce respiratory diseases among the women and their families.

Fig. 10.30 (right) Location of appropriate technology manufacturing projects in India and Kenya.

Fig. 10.31 (below) Stove makers with the Keyo women's group, Kenya.

Not surprisingly, the *upesi* is very popular. The Keyo women's group produce 15 000 stoves a year, using local clay and their traditional skills as potters (Fig.10.31). The stoves are sold in rural markets. As a result, the group members receive a useful source of income and the local community benefits from the employment provided by making stoves. Demand for the stoves is expected to grow, provided certain problems are solved. One problem is the difficulty of transporting the heavy stoves to market. Another is the cost of the raw material, clay. Originally people dug clay locally for free. Now, landowners are charging for the clay.

Between 1973 and 1979 the South Korean government promoted heavy industries such as metals, machinery, chemicals and shipbuilding. This policy proved very successful. The state-sponsored Posco iron and steel company is now the second largest steel maker in the world, and in 1993 South Korea overtook Japan as the world's leading shipbuilder (Fig.11.4).

Since the mid-1980s the emphasis has shifted from heavy industries to cars, high-tech (e.g. semi-conductors) and electronics (TVs, videos etc.). South Korea's four main car makers – Hyundai, Daewoo, Kia and Samsung – aim to produce over 4.5 million cars by the end of the century. This will make South Korea the third largest car maker in the world.

South Korean manufacturing industry is dominated by four huge companies (*chaebols*). Between them, Samsung, Hyundai, Daewoo and LG produce 60 per cent of the country's exports. By 1995 Samsung had become the fourteenth largest company in the world, and the biggest maker of semi-conductors. Unlike American or UK companies, *chaebols* are involved in a range of industries. Apart from semi-conductors, and cars, Samsung makes electronic watches, computers, video recorders, heavy machinery, ships, petrochemicals and medical equipment.

Fig. 11.4 A South Korean shipyard.

Overseas investment

In the 1990s South Korea's *chaebols* began to globalise their operations. The four leading *chaebols* started to invest heavily in the USA and

Fig. 11.5 Globalisation of South Korean *chaebols*.

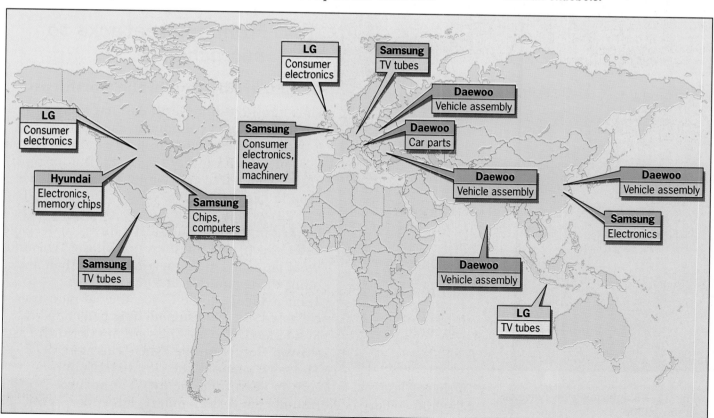

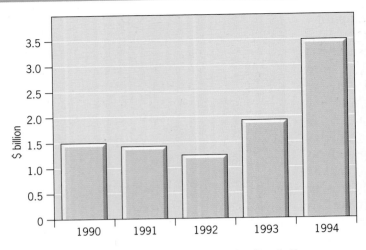

Fig. 11.6 (above) Overseas investment by South Korean companies, 1990-94.

Fig. 11.7 (above) Samsung's factory on Teesside.

EXERCISES

3* Explain the likely reasons for South Korean investment in: • the economically developing world • Europe.

Europe, as well as in East Asia (Fig.11.5). The UK has been South Korea's most popular location in Europe (Fig.11.7). Investment in the UK gives Korean firms a manufacturing base in the EU, which allows them to get round trade barriers. Samsung recently poured £450 million worth of investment into electronics on Teesside. This, the largest Korean investment project in Europe, started production in 1995. Eventually it will employ 3000 people.

CASE STUDY

Fig. 11.8 Shipbuilding on Tyneside in the 1930s.

11.4 From smokestacks to microchips

Deindustrialisation in the North-east

Since the 1930s the North-east has been a problem region. Coal mining, shipbuilding and iron and steel brought prosperity to the region in the nineteenth century (Fig.11.8). But for most of the twentieth century these industries have been in decline. In 1980 County Durham still had 22 working collieries; 25 000 people worked in the iron and steel industry at Teesside and Consett; and the shipyards on the Tyne and Wear launched more merchant ships than any other UK region (Fig.11.9).

Then suddenly in the 1980s, the old industries collapsed. By 1990 shipbuilding had ended at Sunderland. The last shipyard in the North-east – Swan Hunter on the Tyne – closed in 1994. The same year saw the closure of County Durham's last coal mine. Now, apart from the partly re-opened Ellington colliery in Northumberland, deep mining has ended in the

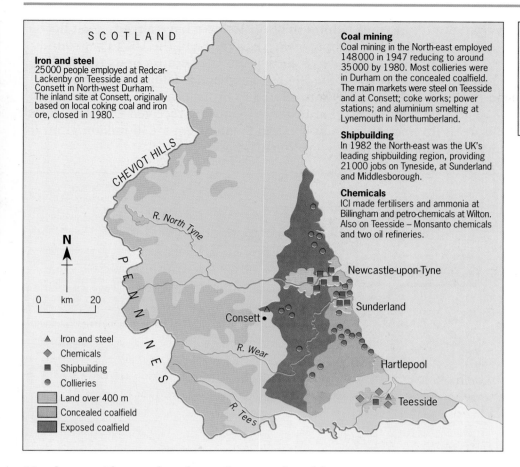

SCOTLAND

Iron and steel
25000 people employed at Redcar-Lackenby on Teesside and at Consett in North-west Durham. The inland site at Consett, originally based on local coking coal and iron ore, closed in 1980.

CHEVIOT HILLS

R. North Tyne

N

0   km   20

P E N N I N E S

Coal mining
Coal mining in the North-east employed 148000 in 1947 reducing to around 35000 by 1980. Most collieries were in Durham on the concealed coalfield. The main markets were steel on Teesside and at Consett; coke works; power stations; and aluminium smelting at Lynemouth in Northumberland.

Shipbuilding
In 1982 the North-east was the UK's leading shipbuilding region, providing 21000 jobs on Tyneside, at Sunderland and Middlesborough.

Chemicals
ICI made fertilisers and ammonia at Billingham and petro-chemicals at Wilton. Also on Teesside – Monsanto chemicals and two oil refineries.

Newcastle-upon-Tyne

Consett •

Sunderland

R. Wear

Hartlepool

R. Tees

Teesside

▲ Iron and steel
◆ Chemicals
■ Shipbuilding
● Collieries
Land over 400 m
Concealed coalfield
Exposed coalfield

Fig. 11.9 The old North-east: the smokestack industries.

North-east. The steelworks at Consett closed in 1980, and though there is still some steel making on Teesside it employs less than half the 1980 workforce. This sudden decline of the region's traditional manufacturing industries is an example of **deindustrialisation**. It hit old industrial regions like the North-east hard. Altogether 160 000 manufacturing jobs were lost in the region between 1970 and 1990. Also, with the closure of factories, large industrial areas became derelict.

The new North-east: reindustrialisation

In little more than a decade the economy of North-east England has undergone a remarkable transformation. By the mid-1990s the region had lost its old image of smokestacks, pit heaps and shipyards. In its place is the new North-east: a region of modern business parks and factories producing electronics and motor vehicles (Fig.11.10).

These changes have come about through foreign investment. By 1995, 380 foreign companies were operating in the North-east. The region is now the biggest centre for investment in Europe by Japanese and South Korean companies. It all started in 1984 when Nissan, the Japanese car maker, decided to build a car assembly plant at Sunderland. Not only did this create over 4000 jobs, it also attracted over 20 parts suppliers (several of them Japanese) to the region. Nissan's success encouraged others. In the next ten years Fujitsu, Samsung, LG,and many smaller firms followed Nissan and located factories in the region.

What are the reasons behind this success? We have already seen how Asian and American companies have invested in the UK to get round EU trade barriers. Many have chosen the UK because of its relatively low wages, and because the English language is familiar. A further incentive has been the grants offered to firms locating in assisted areas. (Table 11.3, Fig. 11.11). For instance, Samsung received £58 million for its Teesside electronics complex, and Siemens got a £30 million grant for its semi-conductor factory on North Tyneside.

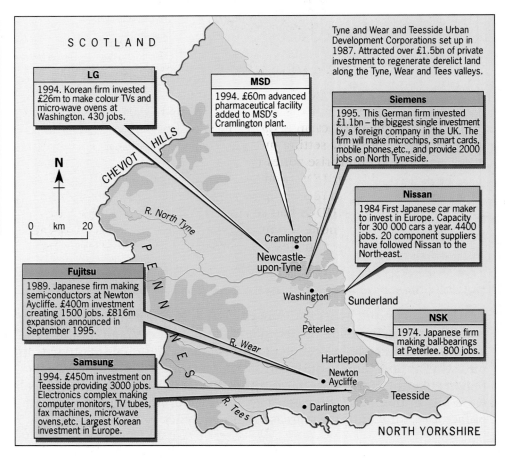

Fig. 11.10 The new North-east: major investments since 1984.

Table 11.2 Foreign investment: advantages and disadvantages for a region

Advantages	Disadvantages
• Creates jobs.	• Factories are controlled from overseas.
• If jobs don't come to the UK they will go to competing countries.	• No control over decisions to close factories.
• Initial investment may attract other firms (e.g. car assembly attracting parts suppliers).	• Foreign firms will compete with UK firms which may be forced out of business.
• Good for the image of a region to attract a major TNC. This may attract further investment.	• Factories are often branch plants. They employ only low skilled workers. There are few highly paid jobs in administration and research and development.
• May introduce new production methods which improve the output of local firms.	
• Boosts exports and helps the country's trade balance.	

Table 11.3 Grants available to firms in assisted areas in 1996

Regional selective assistance	Grants available for the fixed capital costs (machinery, plant) of projects in manufacturing industry and services. Projects must create or safeguard jobs. Grants are not automatic. In development areas they range from 15 – 25 per cent of capital costs. In intermediate areas they cover 10 – 15 per cent of capital costs.
Regional enterprise grants	Grants available for small businesses. The maximum grant for businesses employing up to 25 workers is £15 000. For companies employing up to 50 workers a maximum of £25 000 is available.

Urban development corporations and enterprise zones

In the North-east most traditional heavy industries were concentrated in the lower Tyne, Wear and Tees valleys. Deindustrialisation therefore created a massive dereliction problem in these areas. The government tackled this problem by setting up two urban development corporations (UDCs) and two enterprise zones (EZs).

The Tyne and Wear UDC, and the Teesside UDC were set up in 1987. Their task was to reclaim derelict land and make new sites for industry. By 1995 the UDCs had secured more than £1.5 billion of private investment. Among the major schemes are the East Quayside leisure and office project in Newcastle; the Sunderland enterprise park; and the Hartlepool marina (Fig.11.12).

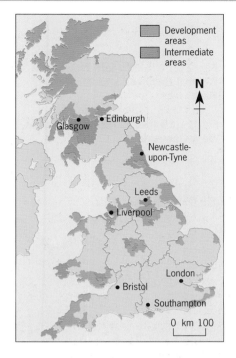

Fig. 11.11 (above) Assisted areas in the UK.

Fig. 11.12 (below) Regeneration of the Tyne and Wear riverbanks.

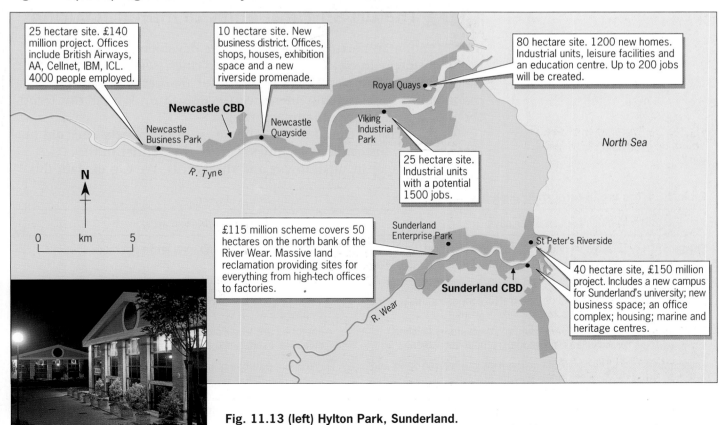

Fig. 11.13 (left) Hylton Park, Sunderland.

The North-east's two EZs also cover derelict riverside areas in Newcastle-upon-Tyne and Sunderland. For ten years (1990-1999), there are special tax allowances and reduced planning controls in these areas. Again the object is to regenerate these areas by bringing in new manufacturing and service industries. The success of the EZ idea was demonstrated at nearby Gateshead. Here one of Europe's largest out-of-town shopping centres – MetroCentre – was built in a former EZ.

Fig. 11.14 (below left) Newcastle Central Business and Technology Park

Fig. 11.15 (below right) Newcastle, West Quayside

11.5 The urban-rural shift of manufacturing

Since 1960, manufacturing industry in the developed world has declined steeply in conurbations and large cities (section 11.4). Meanwhile, in many small towns and rural areas employment in manufacturing has actually increased (section 11.6). We call this trend the urban-rural shift of manufacturing.

As old factories closed in the inner areas of cities, new ones did not replace them. Instead new factories were located either in the outer suburbs, or in small towns and rural areas. We can explain this

Table 11.4 The urban-rural shift: push and pull factors

	Push factors (inner city)	Pull factors (small towns/rural areas
Space	Sites in inner city areas are cramped. Lack of space for single-storey buildings, parking and expansion.	Sites in small towns and rural areas are more spacious.
Cost	Land/rents/taxes are high.	Land/rents/taxes are usually cheaper.
Access	Narrow roads and traffic congestion make access dificult for trucks and for workers' cars.	There is good access to motorways, trunk roads and by-passes.
Buildings	Factories are often old multi-storey buildings, unsuitable for modern production lines.	Factories are single-storey and often purpose-built on industrial estates and business parks.
Environment	The physical environment is often run-down and derelict. There may be problems of vandalism.	Attractive purpose-built estates on greenfield sites. Levels of crime are lower in small towns and rural areas.
Workforce	Inner cities often have a disproportionate number of low-skilled workers.	Skilled and highly qualified workers mainly live in the outer suburbs or in commuter villages and smaller towns.

Fig. 11.16 (above) Hexham in Northumberland

change through the operation of 'push' and 'pull' factors (Table 11.4) combined with the **urban-rural shift** in population (Chapter 5).

11.6 Mid-Wales: rural industrial change

Mid-Wales, comprising the county of Powys and the districts of Ceredigion and Meirionnydd is a remote part of the UK(Fig.11.17). Most of the region is rugged upland and is sparsely populated. Covering nearly 40 per cent of the area of Wales, Mid-Wales has only 7.5 per cent of the country's total population. The population of Mid-Wales peaked in the late nineteenth century. For the next 80 years it fell steadily, until by 1971, there were 40 000 fewer people living in the region. This **depopulation** was due to out-migration. People left Mid-Wales in search of greater job opportunities, higher wages, and better services.

Population revival

Since 1971 Mid-Wales' population has experienced a strong revival (Table 11.5). In some places this was the first recorded population growth for more than a century.

The population increase in Mid-Wales is part of a wider trend known as **counter-urbanisation** (Chapter 6). For the last 25 years people in economically developed countries have been moving out of large cities and conurbations. Most have gone to small towns and

Fig. 11.17 (below) Area covered by the Development Board for Rural Wales.

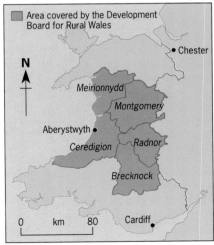

Table 11.5 The population revival in Mid-Wales (% change)

	1961-71	71-81	81-91
Brecknock	–4.5	+4.6	+1.7
Ceredigion	+2.4	+0.8	+10.4
Meirionnydd	–8.4	–3.3	+4.9
Montgomery	–2.5	+10.6	+8.1
Radnor	–1.1	+14.4	+9.8

EXERCISES

8 Study Figure 11.18.
a What sort of businesses is the advert trying to attract?
b What is the main selling point in the advert?
c What sort of image of Mid-Wales is the advert suggesting?

■ BIG RENT SAVINGS - FROM £1.95 PER SQ FT. ■ BIG RATES SAVINGS.
■ BIG CAPITAL GRANT AND LOAN DEALS. ■ BIG ON-GOING
SUPPORT DEALS. ■ BIG LIFESTYLE OPPORTUNITIES.

Fig. 11.18 (above) Development Board advert for Rural Wales.

villages within commuting range of the cities. However, some have moved much further afield, settling in remote regions like the Scottish Highlands and Mid-Wales. They have been attracted by the higher quality of life, away from the congestion, pollution, and crime of large urban areas

Industrial change

In the 1950s the UK government set up a rural development agency in Mid-Wales to deal with the depopulation problem. In 1977 this agency became the Development Board for Rural Wales (DBRW). There is only one other similar body in the UK, which is responsible for the Highlands and Islands of Scotland.

The DBRW aimed to promote Mid-Wales by bringing new manufacturing and service jobs to the region. Grants and low interest loans were given to firms wishing to locate in Mid-Wales. The DBRW also built small factory and office units for sale or rent.

The DBRW was helped by the establishment of a new town (Newtown) in the region in 1968, and by assisted area status for some parts of Mid-Wales (Fig.11.11). So far progress has been impressive. Between 1981 and 1991 there was a 14 per cent increase in manufacturing jobs. This compares with a 25 per cent decrease in the UK as a whole. The DBRW has built eleven business parks across the region (Fig.11.19). In 1995 unemployment in Mid-Wales was 20 per cent below the national average: another indication of the region's success.

Most of the firms locating in Mid-Wales since 1977 have been small businesses. They are extremely diverse, their products range from car components and electronic circuit boards, to processed foods and scientific instruments. In the main firms have gone to the larger centres of population such as Brecon, Cardigan, Newtown and Welshpool. These towns can offer a wide range of services, a skilled workforce, good communications by road, as well as modern factory and office space in purpose-built business parks. Companies moving to Mid-Wales have done so for a variety of reasons. Many small firms see the life style and the high quality of the environment as the major attractions. However, just as important are the availability of greenfield sites, modern factory buildings, low rents and financial assistance.

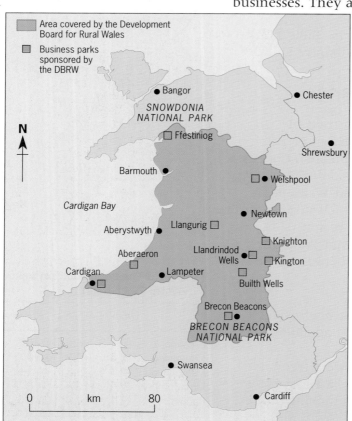

Fig. 11.19 (left) Business parks in Mid-Wales.

11.7 Rotterdam port: locational change

Rotterdam in the Netherlands is the world's number one port. In 1994 it handled nearly 300 million tonnes of cargo. More than three-quarters of this trade was bulk cargo such as crude oil, coal, iron ore and grain. The remaining trade was general cargo – mainly manufactured goods.

Growth of the port

One factor above all others explains the growth of Rotterdam: its geographical situation. It is located near the mouths of two great navigable rivers – the Rhine and Meuse (Maas). This gives it unrivalled access not only to the Netherlands, but also to Germany, eastern France, Belgium and even Switzerland. We call this inland trade area the port's **hinterland** (Fig.11.20).

Thanks to trade between the Netherlands and its overseas colonies, Rotterdam was already a major port by the seventeenth century. However, by the mid-nineteenth century the shallowness of the River Rhine was proving an obstacle to the port's growth. Eventually the problem was solved with the completion of the New Waterway in 1872. This new deep–water (and lock-free) channel linked Rotterdam to the North Sea (Fig. 11.22).

Around this time other developments worked in Rotterdam's favour. In 1868 the Treaty of Mannheim abolished tolls and allowed free navigation on the Rhine. More important was the growth of several large industrial regions in its hinterland– the Ruhr and the Saarland in Germany, Lorraine in eastern France, and South Belgium. Thus Rotterdam's trade expanded as it began to import the raw materials and export the manufactured goods for these new industrial regions.

Because most of its trade is with its international hinterland, we refer to Rotterdam as a **transit** port. Much of the imported cargo is shipped onto Germany, Belgium and other European countries. Most of these cargoes are transported by inland waterways. Also important are pipelines which carry crude oil from Rotterdam to Germany, Antwerp and Amsterdam

Changing location of port activities

Rotterdam's oldest harbours are close to the city centre. Over the last one hundred years the port's trade and busiest harbours have slowly shifted downstream towards the North Sea. They were followed by port industries such as oil refining, petrochemicals, shipbuilding and food processing.

Fig. 11.20 (below) Rotterdam's hinterland.

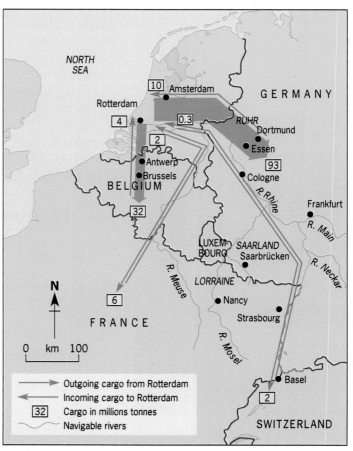

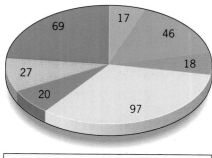

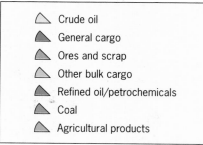

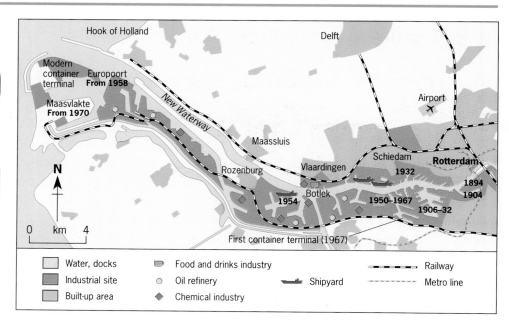

Fig. 11.21 (above left) Throughput of cargo: Rotterdam 1994.

Fig. 11.22 (above right) Rotterdam and Europoort.

Fig. 11.23 (below) Europoort, part of the containerport.

There are two reasons for this movement. First a lack of space. The old, inner harbours were cramped and hemmed-in by existing industries and houses. And second ships have got bigger as new methods of cargo handling have been introduced. Transporting bulk cargoes in large ships reduces costs but requires deep water terminals. Near the mouth of the New Waterway (and for a distance of 40 kilometres out into the North Sea) a navigable channel has been dredged to a depth of 23 metres. This allows the largest oil tankers and bulk carriers (up to 350 000 tonnes) to enter Europoort. General cargoes are mainly transported in standard-sized metal boxes (containers). In 1994 Rotterdam handled more than 3.5 million containers. The advantages of containers are considerable (Table 11.6).

Between 1955 and 1975 the whole of the south bank of the New Waterway, from Rotterdam to the North Sea developed into a port and industrial zone. This area, known as Europoort, has the greatest concentration of oil refineries and chemical works in Europe. Huge areas of flat land also provide storage space for oil, coal, iron ore and containers.

Table 11.6 Advantages of container transport

Cargoes can be loaded and unloaded faster.	Ships spend less time in port and more time at sea earning money. The average container ship only spends 12 per cent of its time in port.
Cargoes can be transferred between different types of transport.	Containers are a standard size. They can be easily loaded onto barges, trains and trucks.
Fewer port workers are needed.	Container handling is highly mechanised.
Cargoes are more secure.	There are few losses of cargo due to spillage, breakage or theft.
Packaging costs are reduced.	Because goods are stored inside metal containers less packaging is needed. Containers are also re-usable.

11.8 Changing location of offices in London

The City and West End of London account for one in seven office jobs in the UK. The City is dominated by financial institutions like the Stock Exchange and the Bank of England (Fig.11.24). Along with New York and Tokyo it is one of the three great financial centres in the world.

The City of London covers little more than three square kilometres. 250 000 people work in this small area in banking, insurance, shipping, commodity dealing and so on. Half of all the world's trading in stocks and shares takes place through the London Stock Exchange, and every day hundreds of millions of pounds pass through the metal, petroleum and commodity markets.

The movement out of the City

In spite of these advantages the City's position is under threat. Many companies are choosing to move out. The attraction is Docklands, just four kilometres to the east. Here office rents are half those in the City and there is plenty of space for new offices which can provide the big dealing floors needed for modern trading.

Canary Wharf

Canary Wharf is part of the London Docklands Urban Development Corporation.(Fig. 11.25). Created in 1981, this UDC had the task of regenerating London's run-down port area. Between 1966 and 1981, closure of London's docks had led to 18000 job losses and massive dereliction.

With its 244 - metre office tower, Canary Wharf is the centre piece of Docklands. By 1995, nearly three-quarters of the office space at Canary Wharf had been occupied. Several banks as well as insurers, advertising agencies and newspapers have successfully moved there from the City. Canary Wharf's early development was hampered by poor communications. Although a new light railway connected Canary Wharf with the City, this soon proved inadequate. Access to the City by road improved with the opening of the Limehouse link and tunnel in 1993. But only when the new Jubilee underground line is complete in 1998 will Canary Wharf's communications compare with the City's.

11.9 Changing location of retailing

Since the 1970s there has been a rapid shift of retailing from the centre to the suburbs of British cities. In 1980 out-of-centre shops and shopping centres accounted for only 5 per cent of sales in the UK. By 1992 this figure had risen to 25 per cent.

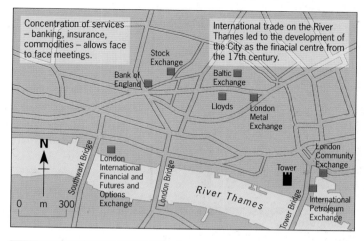

Fig. 11.24 (below) City of London.

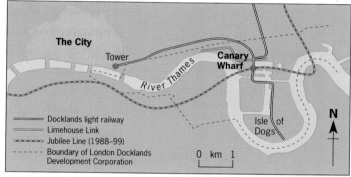

Fig. 11.25 (above) Location of Canary Wharf.

Fig. 11.26 (below) Canary Wharf's tower

Fig. 11.27 Large superstore in Eastbourne.

Fig. 11.28 (below) Regional shopping centres in Britain.

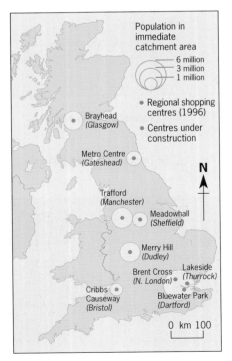

EXERCISES

10 Study Figure 11.30. Describe and explain the distribution of regional shopping centres in Britain.

The first shops to locate in the suburbs were large food superstores (Fig.11.27). Soon they were followed by DIY, furniture and carpet stores. In the suburbs they occupied large 'sheds' on purpose-built **retail parks.** Typically these parks had four or five units and extensive car parking for shoppers.

From the mid-1980s, huge **regional shopping centres** like MetroCentre and Lakeside began to appear. They were enclosed shopping malls, usually built on two levels, with around 200 shops. Most of the shops were familiar high street names (e.g. Marks & Spencer, Boots, Debenhams, etc.) selling comparison goods like clothes and shoes. The new centres also provided cafes, restaurants and cinemas; features such as fountains and glass lifts; and parking for up to 10 000 cars.

Regional shopping centres have proved extremely popular. Merry Hill in the West Midlands is now Europe's largest shopping centre. Until 1994, Oxford Street in London's West End was the UK's most profitable shopping area. In that year it was overtaken by Meadowhall near Sheffield and MetroCentre at Gateshead. Yet despite their success only five regional shopping centres had been completed by 1996. Apart from the four then under construction (Fig.11.28) no others were planned.

Reasons for moving out-of-centre

Retailing, like manufacturing and office activities, has simply followed the movement of people to the suburbs. A suburban location has several advantages for retailers. It gives them access to the better-off and makes it easier for shoppers to use their cars. Compared to the city centre, the suburbs are less congested and have more space for parking. Space is also important for building large superstores and retail sheds. Large sites are either not available or are too expensive in city centres.

However, the main encouragement for the growth of out-of-centre shopping in the UK has been government policy. Planning controls on new shopping developments in the suburbs were lifted in the early 1980s. This led to a rush to build out-of-centre.

The impact

The growth of food superstores led to the closure of one-third of all food shops in the UK between 1972 and 1994. Today food retailers like Sainsbury's and Tesco take over half of all spending on food and everyday household items.

Meanwhile regional shopping centres have devastated retailing in some town centres (Fig.11.33). None has suffered more than Dudley in the West Midlands. Merry Hill opened in 1989 just five kilometres from Dudley town centre (Fig.11.31). Almost overnight most of Dudley's major high street stores moved out to the new centre. Trade fell by 70 per cent. Nearby West Bromwich and Stourbridge were also badly hit. Six years later Dudley had not recovered: second hand shops, discount stores and vacant units dominated the town centre(Fig.11.29).

The growth of new shopping centres has brought other disadvantages. Many occupy greenfield sites on former agricultural land, thus adding to urban sprawl. They create unnecessary car useage, leading to pollution and congestion. Also people without access to a car (usually

Fig. 11.29 (left) Dudley town centre.

Fig. 11.30 (above) Merry Hill centre, Dudley.

the poor and the elderly) are less able to benefit from the lower prices and greater choice available in the new centres.

The response

In the last few years traditional town centres have started to fight back. Town centre shopping malls, built in the 1970s, have been re-furbished; more shopping streets have been pedestrianised; trees have been planted; and services improved. The government also clamped down on new out-of-centre shopping developments. From 1994 developers had to prove that such developments would not damage existing town centres.

EXERCISES

11a What evidence in Figure 11.31 suggests that the centre has become run down?

b* Describe and give a possible explanation for the distribution of low quality shopping areas and shop closures in the city centre.

c* Imagine that you are a town centre manager. Your brief is to regenerate Bradford's central shopping area, which in recent years has become run-down. Study Figure 11.31 and write a report to the City Council describing the current situation and suggesting a plan to revive the central shopping area.

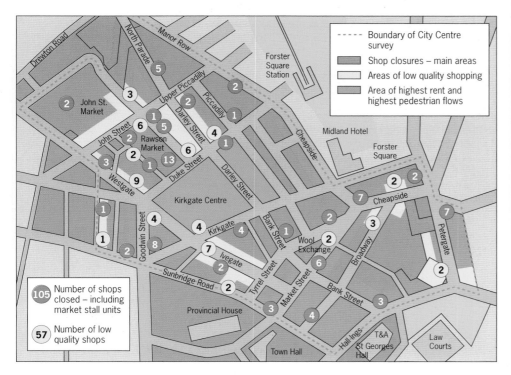

Boundary of City Centre survey

Shop closures – main areas

Areas of low quality shopping

Area of highest rent and highest pedestrian flows

105 Number of shops closed – including market stall units

57 Number of low quality shops

Fig. 11.31 Bradford city centre.

11.10 Summary: Industrial change

Key ideas	Generalisations and detail
Industrial activity is increasingly organised on a global scale.	• Rapid industrial development is occurring in parts of the economically developing world such as the Asian Pacific Rim. TNCs are investing in production worldwide. A global market offers TNCs higher output and lower costs. Global operations also allow TNCs to overcome trade restrictions.
South Korea is a newly industrialising country.	• South Korea has few natural resources for industry. However, it has undergone rapid industrialisation since 1970. Its development has been based on a few very large companies (*chaebols*) e.g. Samsung. In the 1990s these companies started to invest heavily overseas.
Old industrial regions have been hit hard by deindustrialisation.	• Basic industries such as steel, shipbuilding and coal mining declined steeply in regions like central Scotland, South Wales and North-east England, during the 1970s and early 1980s. The result was high rates of unemployment and widespread dereliction.
Re-industrialisation has transformed many old industrial regions.	• Since the mid-1980s there has been massive investment by foreign companies in several old industrial regions in the UK. This investment, encouraged by government grants, has made central Scotland, South Wales and the North-east leading centres of the electronics industry in the EU.
Areas in the UK worst affected by deindustrialisation have been given special status.	• The government has created Urban Development Corporations (UDCs) and Enterprise Zones (EZs) in inner-city and riverside locations. By improving the environment and offering tax breaks, they aim to attract manufacturing and services to run-down industrial areas.
There has been an urban-rural shift of manufacturing industry in economically developed countries.	• Since 1970 manufacturing has declined in conurbations and large cities. New factories have preferred to locate in small towns and rural areas. Lack of space and obsolete factory buildings in large urban areas largely explain this change. Some remote rural areas such as Mid-Wales and the Highlands and Islands of Scotland have benefited from this urban-rural shift. The growth of industry in these areas has been helped by special government agencies and grants.
Port functions and industries have undergone major locational change.	• Revolutions in cargo handling – bulk carriers for oil, coal, ore, grain etc., and containers for manufactured goods – have been responsible for a rapid downstream shift in port activities since 1960. Bulk cargoes and containers are transported in very large ships which need deep water. These cargoes also require large areas of land for storage. Deep water and space are most available near river mouths e.g. Europoort, near Rotterdam.
In economically developed countries retailing has grown in the suburbs at the expense of the CBD.	• Food superstores, retail parks and regional shopping centres have appeared in the suburbs of many British cities since 1980. Retailers have located in the suburbs to be nearer the better-off consumers, to obtain the space needed for large stores and parking and to benefit from less congestion and lower land prices.
The growth of suburban retailing threatens town/city centres.	• Shopping centres in the suburbs compete with retailing in the town/city centre. Smaller town centres such as Dudley have suffered many shop closures. Well known high street retailers have been replaced by second-hand shops and discount stores in the town centre.
Many office activities have moved out-of-centre in British cities.	• Offices have moved out-of-centre to purpose-built office parks in the suburbs. High rents and lack of space for new building have forced many financial services in the City of London to relocate in London's Docklands (e.g, in Canary Wharf).

Glossary

This glossary contains definitions of the technical words, which appear in the book in bold, in the context in which they are used. They are given in alphabetical order.

added value Increase in the value of goods or raw materials through the process of manufacturing.

agribusiness Large-scale, capital-intensive farming based on scientific and business principles.

air mass A large body of air with uniform temperature and humidity characteristics.

anticline A simple upfold of rocks caused by compression in the earth's crust.

anticyclone An area of high pressure. It brings quiet, dry weather, with variable amounts of sunshine and cloud.

aquifer A layer of rock or soil which can hold or carry a lot of water.

aspect The direction in which a slope faces, which often affects the amount of solar radiation it receives.

batholith A very large intrusion of igneous rock within the earth's crust.

bedding plane The boundary separating one layer of a sedimentary rock from another.

biodiversity The number and variety of plant and animal species found in an ecosystem.

biomass The total mass of plant and animal life occurring in a given area.

blockfield A large area of angular boulders that have been broken up by frost action.

brown forest soil Soils found under temperate deciduous forests; the brown colour is due to organic matter (humus).

carrying capacity The maximum number of livestock which can be supported in an area without lasting damage to the environment.

central business district The central area of a town or city which has high land values and is used mostly for business and commercial functions.

comparison goods Goods people buy infrequently after a careful comparison of prices and values, e.g. washing machines. They usually have a high threshold and range.

conservative margin A boundary between two plates which are moving sideways past each other. Crust is neither formed nor destroyed.

constructive margin A boundary between two plates which are moving apart (diverging), and where new oceanic crust (basalt) is forming.

continental drift The theory that the continents have moved position on the earth's surface. The driving force is sea-floor spreading.

continentality The effect of large continental land masses on climate i.e. large mean annual temperature range, summer precipitation maximum.

convectional precipitation Precipitation when warm air rises in thermals or convection currents. Most thunderstorms are formed in this way.

convenience goods Goods people buy frequently and which are relatively cheap. e.g. food. They usually have a low threshold and low range.

core The centre-most part of the earth's interior, comprising a solid inner core and a liquid outer core.

cottage industries Small-scale home-based industries.

counter-urbanisation People moving away from large urban areas to smaller (often rural) settlements.

crust The earth's rocky, outer layer, comprising the continents and ocean basins.

deindustrialisation The decline and closure of traditional industries, such as steel, shipbuilding, coal mining in economically developed countries, which leads to high unemployment and derelict areas.

delta Where a river enters the sea or a lake and deposits its load of sediment. The main river channel splits up into many smaller channels or distributaries.

depopulation An absolute decrease in the population of a place.

depressions Middle-latitude storms. They are low-pressure areas which bring cloud, rain and strong winds.

destructive margin A boundary between two plates which are moving towards each other (converging). One plate plunges below the other and is destroyed in the mantle.

dew-point The temperature at which water vapour condenses to form water droplets.

dispersed settlement pattern A rural settlement dominated by isolated farms.

dyke A small igneous intrusion which cuts vertically through layers of older rock.

economies of scale Cost savings made by production on a large scale.

ecosystem A community of plants and animals which interact with each other and their physical environment.

enterprise The type of farming undertaken by the farmer e.g. cereal growing, dairying.

environmental degradation The adverse effect of farming and population growth on the environment. It includes soil erosion, salination, deforestation, desertification etc.

erosion Wearing away of the land or of the surface of rocks by chemical, physical or biological processes including human overuse.

escarpment A tilted block, with a short steep (scarp) slope and a long gentle (dip) slope.

eutrophication The addition of excess nutrients to lakes and streams, particularly nitrogen and phosphorous. This causes the rapid growth of plants which in turn reduce the oxygen supply in the water.

exfoliation A form of weathering where the surface of a rock peels away in layers.

external economies Cost savings for a firm derived from locating close to suppliers, markets and large urban areas.

faulting The fracturing and movement of rocks caused either by compression or tension in the earth's crust.

folded rocks Rocks bent by compression of the earth's crust.

food chain/food web The transfer of energy in an ecosystem from primary producers to consumers and decomposers. Each organism serves as food for the next in the chain. When organisms eat more than one type of food this links chains in a food web.

food system The chain of activities concerned with producing, processing and selling food.

footloose industries Industries which have few constraints on their choice of location.

fossil fuel Energy resources such as oil, coal and natural gas formed by the decomposition of plants and animals that lived in the geological past.

front A boundary between cold and warm air.

gentrification The movement of middle/high income groups into low-status inner-city areas and the subsequent upgrading of the houses.

geothermal energy The use of hotrocks in the earth's crust to make steam and generate electricity. Sometimes naturally produced steam is harnessed.

geyser A jet of groundwater heated by hot rocks and forced violently to the surface by steam pressure.

global shift The changing location of industry at a global scale - in particular the growing importance of the Pacific Rim and the economically developing world (outside Africa).

globalisation The worldwide location of production by transnational corporations in order to serve a global market and reduce costs.

green belt An area of countryside around a large city in which development is restricted to prevent the growth of urban areas.

greenfield site Sites for industry and commerce previously used only by rural activities (e.g. agriculture).

green wedges An area of agricultural or parkland preserved between spokes of urban development spreading out from a city.

hierarchy A ranking of settlements in a region according to some measure of their importance (e.g. number of services, population etc.).

hinterland The area behind a seaport which supplies the bulk of the exports and to which the bulk of the imports are distributed.

igneous rock A rock formed from the cooling of magma (e.g. granite).

industrial inertia The survival of an industry in an area even though the initial locational advantages, such as local raw materials, have disappeared.

industrial revolution The development of large-scale factory production, originally based on coal and steam power. In the UK it first occurred first between about 1760 and 1830.

initial advantage The reasons why an industry first located in a particular place e.g. the availability of raw materials.

intruded The forcing of magma into the overlying rocks of the earth's crust.

isobars Lines on weather charts joining places of equal air pressure.

just-in-time A system of production where manufacturers supply components to an assembler just a few hours before they are needed on the production line.

karst A limestone landscape.

lahar A high-speed mud flow where volcanic ash mixes with water often from snow or ice melted by the heat of the eruption

land use nucleus, sector, zone see under nucleus, sector, zone

lapse rate The rate at which temperature decreases with height in the lower atmosphere.

lithosphere The term for the earth's crust and the upper part of the mantle.

mantle That part of the earth's interior which is wrapped around the core.

metamorphic rock A rock, which owing to great heat and/or pressure, has been changed from its original state (e.g. slate).

migration The movement of people from one place to another to live permanently.

monoculture The continuous cultivation of a single crop.

newly industrialising countries Countries which have undergone rapid and successful industrialisation since 1970 e.g. South Korea.

nodality The characteristic of a settlement site which is well connected to other places by transport routes.

nucleated settlement pattern A rural settlement pattern dominated by villages where the houses cluster together.

nucleus (land use) An isolated area of distinctive urban land use.

order The position of a settlement within a settlement hierarchy e.g. a hamlet – low order; a city – high order. Also applied to the services found in settlements e.g. convenience – low order; comparison – high order.

organic farming Farming which uses no artificial fertilisers or pesticides.

orographic precipitation Precipitation caused by moist air being forced to rise over hills. Also known as relief precipitation.

plate tectonics The theory that the crust of the earth is divided into a number of separate, rigid plates which are moving all the time. Plate tectonics provides an explanation for such things as earthquakes, volcanoes, fold mountains, rift valleys and continental drift.

podsol The typical soil of coniferous forests: acidic and lacking humus and plant nutrients.

polyculture The cultivation of a wide range of crops.

post-industrial An economy where most of the employment is in service industries - the situation in economically developed countries.

precipitation The deposition of moisture usually from clouds. It includes rain, sleet, snow, frost and dew.

primary producers Green plants which use the sun's energy through photosynthesis to create new tissue which is then used by other members of an ecosystem.

primary sector Economic activities producing raw materials e.g. mining, quarrying, forestry, agriculture, water supply.

primate city The largest city in a country; more than twice as big as the second city.

rain shadow An area on the leeward side of an upland which receives significantly less precipitation than the windward side.

rain-fed agriculture Agriculture which relies solely on direct precipitation.

range The maximum distance people will travel to purchase a particular item or service.

regional shopping centres Very large, enclosed shopping centres mainly selling comparison goods. They are located out-of-centre and have large parking areas e.g. Merry Hill, Meadowhall.

relief The variation in altitude in an area

retail parks Planned shopping centres comprising large retail sheds selling electrical equipment, DIY goods, furniture, food etc. with large parking areas.

rift valley A valley formed by the sinking of land between two parallel fault lines.

rotation The changing cycle of crops grown on farms. Designed to maintain soil fertility and reduce the risk of crop disease.

rural settlement pattern The distribution of settlement in a rural area including the proportion of nucleated and dispersed forms.

rural-urban migration The movement of people from the countryside to live in towns and cities.

secondary sector Manufacturing industries e.g. car making, semi-conductors, iron and steel.

sector (land use) A wedge of distinctive urban land use radiating out from the city centre (often along roads or valleys).

sedimentary rock A rock formed from sediments derived from other rocks (e.g. sandstone) or from the shells and skeletons of organisms (e.g. limestone).

segregation The geographical separation of different income, social and ethnic groups in cities.

sill A small igneous intrusion. which cuts horizontally through layers of older rock.

strata Layers of sedimentary rock.

subduction zone A plate margin where one

plate is being descends (subducts) into the mantle and is destroyed.

subsistence farming When a farmer grows food primarily to feed the family.

sustainability An economic activity which does not use resources faster than natural processes can replenish them.

syncline A simple downfold of rocks caused by compression in the earth's crust.

temperature inversion An increase in temperature with height in the atmosphere (opposite of lapse rate).

tertiary sector Service industries e.g. transport, education, health care, and banking.

topological map A map which consists of a series of lines representing routes and nodes representing places (e.g. stations). It does not show actual distances or real position.

threshold The minimum number of people (or expenditure) needed to support a shop or service in a settlement.

transit port A port where a large percentage of imported cargoes are shipped on to other international destinations.

transnational corporation Very large firms like IBM or General Motors which own businesses in many countries.

transplants Assembly plants set up by foreign-based transnational corporations (e.g. Japanese car manufacturing in the EU).

tropical cyclone (hurricane, typhoon) A powerful tropical storm associated with violent winds and torrential rain.

urban renewal The clearance of sub-standard housing in inner city areas and its replacement with new (often high-rise) housing.

urban sprawl The unplanned expansion of urban areas into the countryside.

urban-rural shift The growing relative importance of small towns and rural areas as centres of industry.

urbanisation An increase in the proportion of the population living in urban areas.

water table The level to which water saturates a porous or permeable rock, or soil.

weather/ing The chemical or physical break-down of rocks by the action of rain, frost, ice, and wind.

wet-point site The location of a settlement which gives access to a water supply (e.g. river, spring, well).

zone (land use) Area of distinctive land use around the city centre.

Index

Index

Series planned by Ela Ginalska, Edited by Gillian Sturgess
Designed by Christie Archer, Picture research by Caroline Thompson
Artwork by Jerry Fowler, Additional artwork by Contour Publishing, Hardlines and Barking Dog Art.

Printed and bound in Hong Kong.

Dedications

MDR: to Edward and Oliver
SS: to Tom and Simon

The authors and publishers would like to thank the following people for help given with information for this book:

J Bryan, A. Shaw and J Ravenscroft of J Tams Ltd; J Crossley, Manor House Farm; BISPA; British Steel Corporation; Ford Education; D Haresign, Marks & Spencer plc; B Hillier, Intermediate Technology; Leicester City Council; A Leuw, IDG, Utrecht; F Lurati, The Riding; MAFF; A Murphy, Self-Help International; National Farmers Union; Northern Development Company; A G Smith; Tyne and Wear Development Corporation; Tyne and Wear PTE; M Worrall, Grange Farm; Welsh Development Agency.

Acknowledgements

Every effort has been made to contact the holders of copyright material, but if any have been inadvertently overlooked, the publishers will be pleased to make the necessary arrangements at the first opportunity.

Photographs
The publishers would like to thank the following for permission to reproduce photographs:

Aerofilms Ltd 147CL; Aerophoto Eelde 184B; Airfotos Ltd 28, 73, 79, 82, 176TR, 181; AP/AAP Photo Library 54; Associated Press 4L, 13; J Allan Cash Photolibrary 96, 100BR, 107R, 154C; ECC International Europe 37R; A Dorst/Environmental Picture Library 68; M Warford/Environmental Picture Library 72; Leslie Garland Picture Library 179, 180; Robert Harding Picture Library 116; A Woolfit/Robert Harding Picture Library 138B; Nigel Cattlin/Holt Studios International 138T; Hulton Deutsch Collection 176BL; Intermediate Technology/Simon L'Epine Exless 170; Intermediate Technology/Neil Cooper 171; London Aerial Photo Library 33, 111, 161, 166, 168, A K Jobbings 26;

Newsteam 187; B Klass/Panos Pictures 53; T Bolstad/Panos Pictures 60; P Tweedie/Panos Pictures 61; R Cousins/Panos Pictures 63B; R Giling/Panos Pictures 129T; Mr R K Pilsbury 38TLC&R,BL&R, 46, 48; Robert Prosser 106; Michael Raw 24, 29, 30, 100TL&CR, 115, 153; Rex Features Ltd 18; J Sainsbury plc 186; Science Photo Library 9, 51, 62, 89; Self Help 140, 142, 143; Sue Shaw 25R, 75, 84, 88, 100CT&BL, 132, 134, 135, 150; SNH Slide Library 70; South American Pictures 103; M Edwards/Still Pictures 64T, 101, 120, 125L, 129C; P Harrison/Still Pictures 117, 144; Gillian Sturgess 21, 35, 41, 69, 74 147CR; Tony Stone Images 38BC, 40, 43, 63T, 64B, 125R, 154TL&C,R&L, 175, 185; J.Tams, plc 157BR; Caroline Thompson 149L, 151C; University of Dundee 50; Tony Waltham/ Geophotos 4C&R, 5R, 6, 14, 15, 16, 17, 19, 22, 25L, 31, 34, 58, 59, 66, 93, 107L, 113, 114, 126, 145, 151B; The Trustees of the Wedgwood Museum, Barlaston, Staffordshire 157; David Woodfall/Wild Images 146, 147B, 148, 149TLCR&C; George Wright 86; Zefa 37L.

Extracts and illustrations:
Dr Philip Amis, 119B, 120T; Bradford Telegraph and Argus, 187B; Craven Herald, 31BR; Daily Record, 12TR; Department of Trade and Industry , 179T; Development Board for Rural Wales, 181R; Dorset County Council, 85; EPA 116T; Geographical Magazine, 59CL, 61BL; Alan Gilbert and the Latin American Bureau, 92; Griffin E. and Ford L., and the Geographical Review 101T, 102; IDG 184TR; New Scientist, 67TL; Rural Development Commission 87BR; Scientific American 145CR; The Economist, 93CR, 108CL; The Guardian, Table, 10, 55, 106B; 118; The Independent 12B, 87T, The Independent Magazine 86C; Times Newspapers Ltd., 11B, 18B.

Maps
Reproduced with the permission of the Controller of Her Majesty's Stationery Office (c) Crown Copyright, extracts from: Grampian & Cairngorms 1992 1:50 000 (page 27); Berwick upon Tweed 1991 1:50 000 (page 77); Dorchester & Weymouth 1993 1:50 000 (page 78); Leicester & Coventry 1994 1:50 000 (page 98).

T = Top, B = Bottom, C = Centre, L = Left, R = Right.